AMERICAN WAR SONGS

Lois B. Cassatt

American War Songs

PUBLISHED UNDER
SUPERVISION OF

*National Committee for the Preservation of
Existing Records of the National Society
of the Colonial Dames of America*

PRIVATELY PRINTED

PHILADELPHIA, PENNSYLVANIA

MCMXXV

Republished by Gale Research Company, Book Tower, Detroit, 1974

784.719
A me

Library of Congress Cataloging in Publication Data
Main entry under title:

American war songs.

Without the music.
1. War-songs, American. I. National Society of the
Colonial Dames of America. II. Title.
[M1628.A6W4   1974]   784.7'19'73   73-19660
ISBN 0-8103-3722-3

THE NATIONAL COMMITTEE
FOR THE
PRESERVATION OF EXISTING RECORDS

ANNOUNCEMENT

THE idea of publishing a book of patriotic war songs was first suggested by Mrs. James Starr, Chairman of the National Record Committee, at a meeting of the National Executive Committee held in Washington in April, 1917. The Congress of the United States had just declared war and the whole country was feverishly eager to contribute what they could to facilitate the efforts of the Government in this momentous event. The delegates present at the meeting voted that the National Society should contribute money to equip a hospital carrier, or carriers, for the Navy. With the idea of assisting in securing the necessary funds, the National Record Committee volunteered the collection and publication of a volume, to be entitled "American War Songs." As might have been expected, the patriotic purpose of the members of the National Society needed no assistance in securing the funds required, and long before the publication could have been completed the money had been distributed through the American Red Cross for purposes of succor to the Navy. During the stress of the war years the thought of publishing the material collected by the National Committee was set aside, all feeling that every moment should be devoted to the daily needs of our soldiers at home and abroad.

At the outset of the project, the Chairman of the National Record Committee invited the Corporate Societies to send songs they felt worthy of being included in the book, asking that authentic historic data accompany such songs. As practically all of the Corporate Societies responded to this request, the "American War Songs" may truly be said to be the result of the effort of all, rather than the product of any one group. Especial reference, however, should be made to the contributions received from the Maine, Illinois, Texas, New York, Maryland and Pennsylvania Societies, and appreciation expressed for the great interest displayed by Mrs. Albert Souissat, Miss Cornelia Williams — up to the time of her death — Miss Alice French and Mrs. William Todd Robins, all former Historians of the

National Society. The far scattered residences of the members of the Committee have made meetings impossible, which must be the excuse for the Chairman assuming the responsibility of the compilation and publication of this volume.

The dedication of the volume to the memory of Mrs. Alexander J. Cassatt, who for so many years served the National Society as its Treasurer, was approved at the 1923 Biennial Council. At this same Council, Mrs. William Ruffin Cox, the Honorary President of the National Society, consented to have included in this book the Memorial which she presented to the memory of Mrs. Cassatt at the 1921 Council. Mrs. Joseph Rucker Lamar, National President, has furnished a brief sketch of the work of Mrs. Cassatt in our National Organization, and the resolutions adopted by the Pennsylvania Society, prepared by Mrs. James D. Winsor, a former President and one of the Founders of the Pennsylvania Society, and Miss Anne Hollingsworth Wharton, also a Founder of the Pennsylvania Society, a former Historian of the National Society, are also included. Mrs. Cassatt always showed great interest in the work of the preservation of records, and was largely responsible for establishing this work as part of our permanent national program.

The photograph which appears in the front of this volume is taken from a portrait of Mrs. Cassatt by Julian Storey, and presented for the purpose by Mrs. W. Plunket Stewart, Mrs. Cassatt's daughter.

Mr. William Bond Wheelwright, of Boston, author of the "Introduction," undertook the task of collecting the historic data in the hands of the Committee, dividing the songs into the Nation's respective war periods. For his treatment of the subject the Committee is greatly indebted.

Mr. Edgar B. Sherrill, of the firm of McGrath-Sherrill Press, on whose press the volume has been printed, has been untiring in his efforts to secure the best results for this volume. The Committee is deeply indebted to him for the cover design, the type used and the superior binding, which are so largely responsible for the satisfactory results attained.

The National Committee takes this opportunity of expressing thanks and appreciation for the courtesies extended them in the granting of privileges to procure material, to the following: Officers of the Congressional Library at Washington, The Pennsylvania State Library at Harrisburg, the Boston Athenæum, the Pennsylvania Historical Society, J. B. Lippincott & Co., Publishers, Theodore Presser, Musical Publisher, and Mr. E. C. Mills of the Music Publishers Protective Association.

Respectfully submitted,

MEMBERS OF THE COMMITTEE,

Sarah Logan Wister Starr

Chairman, National Record Committee

DEDICATION

THIS volume of war songs is dedicated to the memory of a loved woman who was herself a "Happy Warrior" — not only ready to give battle for what she believed in, but that rarer thing — a leader of others in maintaining the highest standards that we possess.

Mrs. Alexander J. Cassatt, born Lois Buchanan, a niece of the fifteenth President of the United States, was appointed, in 1901, to the office of Treasurer of the National Society of the Colonial Dames of America, by its second President, Mrs. Howard M. Townsend, of New York. At the following Council, in 1902, she was formally elected to that office, and regularly reëlected, without opposition, at every succeeding Council until her death in 1920.

Mrs. Townsend was singularly successful in the numerous appointments that she made during her long term of office, but in none was she more truly inspired than in the selection of Mrs. Cassatt for the important position of Treasurer; for she was gifted in matters of finance, and her reports solicited not only the approval but the warm commendation of the experts who examined them.

The nineteen years during which she served in this office were important ones in the history of the Society. They included the restoration of the Old Church at Jamestown in Virginia and the building of the Memorial at Arlington to the soldiers and sailors who fell in the Spanish-American War. The fireproof case which contains the Record Book in the Arlington Mansion was made from a design which she furnished.

These years included the display of valuable loan exhibits at more than one National Exposition; the publication of important books of reference and of unpublished documents; the purchase, in advance, of rooms for the Society Headquarters in the George Washington Memorial Building; the relief work accomplished during the World War and the equipping of hospital ships for the Navy; the preliminary plans for the Memorial at Plymouth, and the beginning of the Endowment Fund for the restoration and maintenance of Sulgrave Manor, in England. Her letter, enclosing our first donation to that fund, still hangs on the walls at Sulgrave, in testimony that it was the first contribution sent for that purpose from America.

This was also a period of development in the Society itself, and the relations between the Societies in Colonial and non-Colonial States were satisfactorily adjusted and put upon a stable foundation.

In all these accomplishments Mrs. Cassatt had an active share, and her aid and counsel were eagerly sought and faithfully followed by her fellow officers.

She was possessed of a courage rarer in women than in men; especially in women reared as she was, to the strict observance of the courtesies and amenities of life. She never hesitated to voice an unpalatable truth, when it needed to be spoken, but she was able to do it without giving offense. She did not shrink from supporting an unpopular cause, when she was convinced of its righteousness; and yet her wisdom was informed with a saving sense of humor which is sometimes the greatest wisdom.

All that the National Society owes her cannot be put into words, but it is both a pleasure and a privilege to give this meagre expression of our grateful appreciation of her worth.

Clarinda P. Lamar

(MRS. JOSEPH R. LAMAR)
*President of the National Society
of the Colonial Dames of America*

MEMORIAL[1]

ONE of the touching word pictures of our New Testament is the description of the grief of the friends of the dead Tabitha, by interpretation Dorcas, as they displayed the coats and garments which she made when with them. The spiritual coats and garments of our lamented Treasurer I would show to the Council of the National Society of the Colonial Dames of America today.

Knowing little of the early days of Mrs. Cassatt, I turned to her daughter for aid, and she kindly sent me a brief personal history written by Mrs. Cassatt for her children, which is so exquisitely simple and touching that I transcribe it *verbatim* for you.

"In October, 1867, my brother James Buchanan, who was the eldest of the family, invited Henrietta and me to pay him a visit in Titionti, Pennsylvania, a small town in the then busy oil region of the state, on the Allegheny River between Oil City and Irvington. He was practicing law, and also interested with thousands of others in the oil wells in the vicinity. Mr. Alexander J. Cassatt was stationed at the time at Irvington and was the superintendent of the Warren and Franklin Branch of the Pennsylvania Railroad.

"He was with us a great deal, and we went up to Irvington and paid a short visit to his home, where his father, mother and sister were living with him. After a delightful visit during which we took long rides on horseback through the country, we started home, stopping on the way to see Niagara Falls. Before we reached home, I had become engaged to your father.

"On my return home the question was submitted to my parents, and my father, thinking I was too young to be married, prevailed upon me to wait until after a promised visit to Baltimore the following winter, saying that if we were then of the same mind, he would consent to our marriage. Before going to Baltimore, I paid a visit to my Uncle James Buchanan, the ex-presi-

[1]*Memorial to Lois Buchanan Cassatt.* Read by Mrs. William Ruffin Cox, of Virginia, before the National Society of the Colonial Dames of America, at the Biennial Council of 1921.

dent, and while there your father came to pay his respects to my uncle, having been invited by him to come. After this visit, Uncle James urged me to be married at once, saying that he was perfectly satisfied with the young man. This, however, was not agreed to by my parents and I went to Baltimore, and remained there until the time of my Uncle James Buchanan's death in 1868. Your father came to Baltimore several times while I was there, and I saw nothing to make me change my mind in regard to him.

"After my uncle's death, I with all my family went to Wheatland for the funeral. I then returned to Oxford Rectory, and preparations were begun for my marriage. In the spring of 1868, your father was made superintendent of Motive Power and moved to Altoona, where he had one of the Company's houses assigned to him, just back of the Logan House. In October, my mother and I went with him to Altoona to see the house and arrange some details about the furniture. We were married in Trinity Church, Oxford, on Wednesday, November 25, at twelve o'clock. The day was bright and cold and by the time breakfast in the Rectory was over, it was snowing hard. We left the Rectory at three o'clock for New York. My father drove us to the station at Oxford, and waited to see us off on the train.

"After a delightful trip to New York and Boston, we went to our new home at Altoona about the fifth of December. There we found everything in readiness for our reception, my sister Henrietta and Lydia Cassatt having prepared a good dinner. Our household consisted of a colored cook and waitress combined, and one man in the stable, James Fagan. He remained a servant and pensioner until his death in 1907. Thus began a long and happy married life for me full of incident and vicissitudes of every kind."

This lovely relation of her happy betrothal and marriage makes such a true and eloquent memorial to our lamented Treasurer that I could not omit it.

Mrs. Cassatt's life became a brilliant and philanthropic reality. Her husband's phenomenal success soon enabled them to build the beautiful home in Haverford where many of us happily remember her as its gracious and hospitable hostess. There her broad sense of patriotism and charity pervaded and inspired the social allurements which she was so fitted to enjoy. The National Society of the Colonial Dames of America was the first important outside work to which she gave her time and thought. Thereafter she led many social, educational and charitable organizations, but to her life's end, home was her most sacred realm, and no duties, social or civic, ever caused her to fail in loving care of husband and children. While the latter were young rarely were they sent to bed without their happy half-hour of stories read aloud, or sweet songs sung in her wonderfully touching and true voice. Year after year, she held in her home a little Sunday class for her own and a few neighboring children.

Dullness never existed where she was. Her keen sense of humor and her rare gift for turning the smallest incident into an amusing tale, made daily life a delight to all around her. This attractive quality combined with firmness when occasion called for it, and loving patience at all times created a home atmosphere never to be forgotten by those who shared it.

On March 19, 1921, a memorial baptistry was dedicated to her in the Church of the Redeemer, Bryn Mawr, by her family. The inscription on the bronze tablet is:

TO THE GLORY OF GOD AND IN LOVING MEMORY OF
LOIS BUCHANAN CASSATT

Kate Cabell Cox

TRIBUTES

THE following tributes to Mrs. Alexander J. Cassatt, presented to the Pennsylvania Society of the Colonial Dames of America, at its regular meeting on January 21, 1920, by Mrs. James D. Winsor, a former President and one of the Founders of the Pennsylvania Society, and Miss Anne Hollingsworth Wharton, also a Founder of the Pennsylvania Society, respectively, were adopted and embodied in resolutions:

It is with deep sorrow, that we offer a tribute to the memory of Mrs. Alexander J. Cassatt, formerly our President. For many years she was an earnest member of our Society. A woman with clear judgment, a well-balanced mind, of great dignity of character, she was eminently fitted to guide the affairs of our Society.

Although naturally reserved, those who enjoyed her friendship knew well the warmth and depth of her affection, and we feel that our loss is very great.

A woman that feareth the Lord, she shall be praised, and let her own works praise her in the gates.

Rebecca Winsor

The officers and members of the Pennsylvania Society of the Colonial Dames of America desire to express to the family of Mrs. Alexander J. Cassatt their deep and heartfelt sympathy in their great loss. For themselves, they feel that they have lost a valued member and counsellor.

A member of the Pennsylvania Society since 1894, sometime its Treasurer, and for over ten years its honored President, Mrs. Cassatt brought to the Councils of this Society, and to those of the National Society of the Colonial Dames of America of which she has been Treasurer since 1901, great executive ability, dignity, moderation and rare common sense.

Many difficult problems were satisfactorily solved during her leadership, important work was accomplished, notably the organization of a number of County Committees through the State of Pennsylvania, a work dear to her heart, for the patriotic interest which it has aroused through the State, which led to the preserving and marking of historic buildings and sites.

To all of the undertakings of this Society, Mrs. Cassatt gave unsparingly of her thought, her time and her strength. As the years go by we shall realize more and more how much we owe to the ability, wisdom and foresight of the fifth President of the Pennsylvania Society of the Colonial Dames of America, Mrs. Alexander J. Cassatt.

Anne Hollingsworth Wharton

INTRODUCTION

THE compilation of a book of "American War Songs" at once evolves some extremely interesting problems connected with music. In order to grasp their full significance it is necessary to detach ourselves temporarily from the thought of any specific song or songs, and to consider music in general and war songs in particular, subjectively.

Man might be defined as the only mammal that sings.

According to Darwin music is the result of sexual selection. Those of our prehuman ancestors who could sing best were drawn as mates by the opposite sex. The emotions of love, rivalry and combat incident to the breeding season were thus associatively welded to the perception of tones, so that we in listening to music have called up vaguely and indefinitely strong emotions of a long past age.

According to Spencer on the other hand, the art owes its striving power to its suggestions of excited and emotional speech. The cadences of music are an intensification of those of language and arouse the corresponding emotions in exaggerated form.

The new school of psychologists will doubtless find much to sympathize with in both these views. Albert Gehring, author of "The Appreciation of Music," reduces to five the number of causes for deriving pleasure from music. "The elementary power of tone, form, association, symbolization and sympathetic agitation through parallelism of tonal process. There is an effect of tones," he says, "which is purely physiological in nature, and insusceptible of further analysis. Structural beauties are a source of distinct delight. . . . associations are involved, symbolizations play their part and there are numerous points of resemblance between the flow of tones and the flow of thought and feeling." It would seem as if the peculiarly unique and intense enjoyment afforded by music when it thrills us to the core must likewise be due to a unique cause, or it may be to a combination of causes. What this is, has so far not been satisfactorily explained. However, the most promising suggestions are those which have been offered by the "symbolistic" and "parallelistic" theories.

A modern recognition of these phenomena, though not by scientists, is the universal employment of music at motion picture theatres to parallel the action of the players and to intensify the emotional enjoyment of the spectators.

Music by some is considered to have a therapeutic value, and its use in hospitals is not unknown. At the modern banquet under the ban of prohibition, it has somewhat taken the place of libation as a stimulant and means of evolving a convivial spirit. Modern athletic contests are characterized by organized singing to an extent unknown a couple of generations ago. As an offset to fatigue and an incentive to physical effort, music of some sort has long been cherished. The old-time sailor works the better under the stimulus of a rollicking chantey; and is there a man that has ever carried a gun on a weary march, who cannot testify to the wonderful effect of a band, or even of a fife and drum? Or is there a woman who has not exceeded her natural desire for exercise, under the bewitching summons of a Strauss waltz or a snatch of modern jazz?

Dr. Frank Damrosch declares that "The joy which a child gets in reproducing beautiful melodies is like no other experience in life. In the process of doing so, its whole being, body, mind, heart and soul is engaged. The song for the moment *is* the child."

Regardless of whether we conclude to ascribe with Darwin the origin of the instinctive urge of music to sexual selection, or accept the theories of some other scientists or psychologists, we may unaminously agree that music is an incentive to action, and as such has given rise to the war song.

The second consideration which may claim our attention before perusing the "American War Songs," is the extent to which they may reflect material characteristics as they existed at different periods of our country's development. In perusing these songs we should bear in mind the homogeneity of our citizenship in the days of the Revolution and "Yankee Doodle," contrasted with the conglomerate character of the population reflected in legions of "Yanks" that were "Coming Over There" in the World War. We should recall that the first of these songs were representative of a population under four million, and the last were sung by an equal number of soldiers who had gone to fight for the more than one hundred million people left at home.

Nor should we overlook the influence of modern communication in welding so vast a population together, in contrast to the obstacles to communication over which the colonies struggled into a state of national cohesion.

William Bond Wheelwright

CONTENTS

CHAPTER I
REVOLUTIONARY WAR

CHAPTER II
WAR OF 1812

CHAPTER III

MEXICAN WAR

CHAPTER IV

CIVIL WAR

CHAPTER V

SPANISH–AMERICAN WAR

CHAPTER VI

WORLD WAR

Contents

ILLUSTRATIONS

COLONIAL SONGS
AND
REVOLUTIONARY SONGS

AMERICAN WAR SONGS

CHAPTER I

COLONIAL SONGS AND REVOLUTIONARY SONGS

ALTHOUGH the early American Colonists had their songs such as the Pilgrim Forefathers' song, which might be classified as a folk song, there is scarcely any record of war songs of this period. This will be explained by the nature of their stealthy enemies, the Redskins, against whose raids an equally stealthy form of attack was necessary.

Then again the armed bands were comparatively small in number and all the circumstances of their life forced them into close offensive and defensive alliances as a matter of self-preservation. In other words, there did not exist the same necessity of finding more or less artificial methods of sustaining the morale and fighting spirit of their troops.

Nevertheless, there have come down to us a few songs of pre-revolutionary days that may fairly be included in this volume.

Lydia Bolles Newcomb, in an article on "Songs and Ballads of the Revolution," says that in 1768 the song "In Freedom We're Born" was sold at the Boston Book Store, King Street, Boston, the words being as follows:

PATRIOT'S APPEAL

Come join hand in hand brave Americans all,
Awake through the land at fair Liberty's call.
No tyrannous acts shall suppress your just claim,
Or stain with dishonor America's name.

REFRAIN

In freedom we're born, in freedom we'll live,
Our purses are ready, steady friends, steady,
Not as slaves but as freemen our money we'll give.

Our worthy forefathers, let's give them a cheer,
To climates unknown did courageously steer;
Through oceans to deserts for freedom they came,
And, dying, bequeathed us their freedom and fame.

The tree their own hands had to Liberty reared
They lived to behold growing strong and revered;
With transport they cried "How our wishes we gain
For our children shall gather the fruits without pain."

Then join hand in hand brave Americans all,
By uniting we stand, by dividing we fall.
In so righteous a cause we may hope to succeed,
For Heaven approves every generous deed.

Rev. Henry Archer's "Volunteer Boys" was a convivial song and very popular at the time.

THE VOLUNTEER BOYS

Hence with the lover who sighs o'er his woe
　　Chloes and Phyllises toasting,
Hence with the slave who will whimper and whine
　　Of ardor and constancy boasting,
　　　　Hence with love's joys,
　　　　Follies and noise,
The toast that I give is Volunteer Boys.

Nobles and beauties and such common toasts
　　Those who admire may drink, sir;
Fill up the glass to the volunteer host,
　　Who never from danger will shrink, sir,
　　　　Let mirth appear
　　　　Every heart cheer,
The toast that I give is the brave volunteer.

Here's to the squire who goes to parade,
　　Here's to the citizen soldier;
Here's to the merchant who fights for his trade,
　　Whom danger increasing makes bolder.

Let mirth appear
Union is here
The toast that I give is the brave volunteer.

Here's to the lawyer who, leaving the bar
Hastens where honor doth lead, sir;
Changing the gown for the ensigns of war,
The cause of his country to plead, sir.
Freedom appears,
Every heart cheers,
And calls for the health of the law volunteers.

Here's to the soldier, though battered in wars
And safe to his farmhouse retired;
When called by his country ne'er thinks his scars,
With ardor to join is inspired.
Bright fame appears
Trophies uprear,
To veteran chiefs who became volunteers.

Here's to the farmer who dares to advance
To harvests of honor with pleasure;
Who with a slave the most skillful in France
A sword for his country would measure.
Hence with cold fear,
Heroes rise here,
The ploughman is changed to the stout volunteer.

Here's to the peer, first in senate and field,
Whose actions to titles add grace, sir,
Whose spirit undaunted would never yet yield
To a foe, to a pension, or place, sir.
Gratitude here,
Toasts to the peer,
Who adds to his title "the brave volunteer."

Thus the bold bands for old Jersey's defense
The muse hath with rapture review'd, sir;
With our volunteer boys, as our muses commence,
With our volunteer boys, they conclude, sir.
Discord or noise
Ne'er damp our joys,
But health and success to our volunteer boys.

And William Billings fulminates as follows in "Chester":

CHESTER

Let tyrants shake their iron rod,
  And slavery clank her galling chains;
We fear them not; — we trust in God —
  New England's God forever reigns.

Howe and Burgoyne and Clinton, too,
  With Prescott and Cornwallis join'd,
Together plot our overthrow,
  In one Infernal league combin'd.

When God inspir'd us for the fight,
  Their ranks were broke, their lines were forc'd,
Their ships were shatter'd in our sight,
  Or swiftly driven from our coast.

The Foe comes on with haughty stride,
  Our troops advance with martial noise
Their Vet'rans flee before our youth
  And Gen'rals yield to beardless boys.

What grateful off'ring shall we bring
  What shall we render to the Lord?
Loud Hallelujahs let us sing,
  And praise His name on ev'ry chord.

The Boston Tea Party was celebrated in a song sung to the tune of "Hosier's Ghost."

THE BOSTON TEA PARTY

As near beauteous Boston lying on the gently swelling flood,
Without jack or pennant flying three ill-fated teaships rode.
Just as glorious Sol was setting, on the wharf a num'rous crew,
Sons of freedom, fear forgetting, suddenly appeared in view.

Armed with hammers, axes, chisels, weapons new for warlike deed,
Towards the taxed tea freighted vessels they approached with dreadful
    speed.

O'er their heads aloft in mid sky three bright angel forms were seen;
This was Hampden, that was Sidney, with fair Liberty between.

"Soon," they cried, "your foes you 'll banish,
Soon the triumph shall be won;
Hence the setting sun shall vanish ere the glorious deed be done."
Quick as thought the ship was boarded, hatches burst and chests dis-
    played;
Axes, hammers, help afforded; what a crash that eve they made.

Deep into the sea descended cursèd weed of China's coast;
Thus at once our fears were ended; British rights shall ne'er be lost.
Captains! Once more hoist your streamers, spread your sails and plough
    the wave;
Tell your masters they were dreamers when they thought to cheat the
    brave.

There was a ballad of thirteen stanzas on the death of Nathan
Hale, who was executed as a spy.

BALLAD ON THE DEATH OF NATHAN HALE

The breezes went steadily through the tall pines
    A-saying "Oh hu-ush" a-saying "Oh hu-ush,"
As stilly stole by a bold legion of horse
    For Hale in the bush, for Hale in the bush.

"Keep still," said the thrush as she nestled her young,
    In a nest by the road; in a nest by the road,
"For the tyrants are here, and with them appear
    What bodes us no good, what bodes us no good."

The brave captain heard it and thought of his home,
    In a cot by the brook; in a cot by the brook.
With mother and sister, and memories dear,
    He so gaily forsook; he so gaily forsook.

Cooling shades of the night were coming apace,
    The tattoo had beat; the tattoo had beat.
The noble one sprang from his dark lurking place,
    To make his retreat; to make his retreat.

He warily trod on the dry rustling leaves,
　　As he passed through the woods; as he passed through
　　　　the woods,
And silently gained his rude launch on the shore,
　　As she played with the flood; as she played with the
　　　　flood.

The guards of the camp, on that dark, dreary night,
　　Had a murderous will; had a murderous will,
They took him and bore him afar from the shore,
　　To a hut on the hill; to a hut on the hill.

No mother was there, nor a friend who could cheer,
　　In that little stone cell; in that little stone cell;
But he trusted in love from his Father above,
　　In his heart all was well; in his heart all was well

An ominous owl, with his solemn bass voice,
　　Sat moaning hard by; sat moaning hard by,
"The tyrant's proud minions most gladly rejoice,
　　For he must soon die; for he must soon die."

The brave fellow told them, no thing he restrained —
　　The cruel gen'ral; the cruel gen'ral,
His errand from camp, of the ends to be gained,
　　And said that was all; and said that was all.

They took him and bound him and bore him away,
　　Down the hill's grassy side; down the hill's grassy side,
'Twas there the base hirelings, in royal array,
　　His cause did deride; his cause did deride.

Five minutes were given, short moments, no more,
　　For him to repent; for him to repent,
He pray'd for his mother, he asked not another
　　To heaven he went; to heaven he went.

The faith of a martyr, the tragedy show'd,
　　As he trod the last stage; as he trod the last stage,
And Britons will shudder at gallant Hale's blood,
　　As his words do presage; as his words do presage.

Thou pale king of horrors, thou life's gloomy foe,
  Go frighten the slave; go frighten the slave,
Tell tyrants, to you their allegiance they owe;
  No fears for the brave; no fears for the brave.

Dr. Hamilton Mabie mentions a song of sentiment which first appeared in the *Pennsylvania Magazine*, also *New Hampshire Freeman's Journal*, 1776, which attained wide popularity and was sung long after the surrender at Yorktown:

THE LIBERTY SONG

As Collinet and Phœbe sat
Beneath a poplar grove,
The gentle youth, with fondest truth,
Was telling tales of love.

But Phœbe stirs him to deeds of valor, sends him to the war and promises to marry him on his return.

Here is one from New Hampshire (*Freeman's Journal*, 1776):

Hark, hark, the sound of war is heard,
And we must all attend.
Take up our arms and go with speed
Our country to defend.

Maryland, as one of the border states, was constantly threatened by the vicissitudes of the French and Indian War, and troops were sent out from time to time under the command of the War Governor, Maj.-Gen. Horatio Sharpe. There was not much time for poetry or for song-singing, but we are fortunate in retaining one of their lays written by an officer of the Maryland Independent Company, September, 1754. The air was that of a very popular Jacobite song, "Over the Hills and Far Away," a survival of the wild and passionate enthusiasm for the Stuarts, which had so fatal an ending.

INDIAN WAR SONG

Over the Hills with Heart we go,
To fight the proud insulting foe,
Our country calls and we'll obey
Over the Hills and far away.

CHORUS

Over the Mountains' dreary waste,
To meet the enemy we haste,
Our King commands and we 'll obey,
Over the Hills and far away.

Whoe'er is bold, whoe'er is free
Will join and come along with me,
To drive the French without delay
Over the Hills and far away.

CHORUS

Over the rocks and over the steep,
Over the waters, wide and deep,
We'll drive the French without delay,
Over the Hills and far away.

On fair Ohio's Banks we stand,
Musket and bayonet in hand,
The French are beat, they dare not stay,
But take to their heels, and run away.

CHORUS

Over the rocks and over the steep,
Over the waters, wide and deep,
We'll drive the French without delay
Over the Hills and far away.

But, alas! It was not the French who ran. Braddock's defeat was disastrous. The French and savages came within thirty miles of Baltimore and the men carried their wives and children out to the ships in the harbor to save them from the dreadful fate of the countryside in Western Maryland.

Maine knew full well the meaning of armed encounter with the depredating Indian tribes, incited frequently by the French. The invasion of Acadia led by Governor Shirley in 1755, and the Louisburg Expedition of 1758 claimed many of her sons and doubtless inspired the following "Battle Song," by Emma Huntington Nason, furnished by the Maine Society.

BATTLE SONG
A BALLAD OF BRITTANY
BY EMMA HUNTINGTON NASON

Mrs. Charles H. Nason (Emma Huntington Nason), a poet of note and a member and historian of the National Society of Colonial Dames of America in Maine, born in Hallowell, Maine, in 1845; died 1921. Permission to print in this volume was given by Mrs. Nason.

With eyes afire and hearts aflame, the valiant peasant host,
From Tréguier and good Saint Pol, marched up the Breton Coast.
"Sing us our Father's battle-song," the standard-bearer said,
"And let the cursed invader know, 'King Arthur is not dead!'
The song that every mother's tongue and every maiden fair,
A thousand years and more have sung from Orne to Finistèrre!
The song by which the Cymric chiefs their ancient battles won,
That we, as they, the foe may slay before the turn of sun!
"A foeman's heart for every eye! a head for every arm!"

The valleys and the mountain-tops know well the wild alarm!
'Three lives for one!' by grassy mound and by the cromlech's mould,
And 'blood for tears,' shall dew the ground as in the days of old!
Sing, comrades mine! the sea-lights shine where flies the banner red!
As long ago, we greet the foe: 'King Arthur is not dead!' "

With eyes afire and hearts aflame, from o'er the English Sea,
A band of brave Welsh mountaineers marched down through Brittany.
"We strike for England," was the cry, "before the turn of noon,
But live or die, fling out on high the ancient battle-tune!
The song that for a thousand years has floated on the gale,
From Snowdon heights and Harlech lights to far Glamoran's Vale;
The song our Celtic sires loved, in days that long have fled,
That mothers to their first born sung: 'King Arthur is not dead!'
And like a royal chant of old, rang out the martial strain!
But hark! — a pause — and from afar comes back the grand refrain.

And where the borders of Saint Cast their broken ridges trace,
The invader and the Breton-born stood grimly face to face.
"King Arthur is not dead!" the one in rhythmic cadence cries,
"King Arthur is not dead — not dead!" the Breton host replies.

"Halt! fire!" the English captain shouts.
Nor hand nor musket stirred;
And "Fire!" rings down the Breton lines; yet no man heeds the word;
For all who march to Arthur's call are of one kith and kin;
No feud have they, no foe to slay, no strife to lose or win!
But heart to heart, and hand to hand, the weeping soldiers stood,
Whose one ancestral song had proved their common brotherhood.
Ay! tears for blood! Thus shall it be from Orne to Finisterre,
With love for hate from Snowdon's hills unto Glamoran fair
And peace for strife, throughout the world, and right in place of wrong,
When men shall learn their brotherhood through one Immortal Song.

The last Colonial War has been called "The Dunmore War."
Its one battle was fought at the mouth of the Kanawha River,
on the present site of Point Pleasant, West Virginia. The engagement is sometimes referred to as "The Battle of Point Pleasant"
and sometimes "The Battle of the Great Kanawha," and was
fought by eleven hundred Virginians, commanded by Gen.
Andrew Lewis, who had been sent out by Lord Dunmore, the
last royal governor of Virginia, to battle with the Indians under
their chief, Cornstalk. English oppression had caused discontent
in the Colonies for some time and historians have suggested that
the Indians may have been egged on in their depredations that
the Colonies might be weakened. The flower of "The Valley of
Virginia" met the Indians in bloody battle, October 10, 1774,
at Point Pleasant and won a dearly bought victory. The following verses were found many years after the battle in the Bible
of the Lewis Family.

THE BATTLE OF POINT PLEASANT[1]

Ye daughters and sons of Virginia incline
    Your ears to a story of woe;
I sing of a time when your fathers and mine
    Fought for us on the Ohio.

In seventeen hundred and seventy-four,
    The month of October, we know,
An army of Indians, two thousand or more,
    Encamped on the Ohio.

The Shawnees, Wyandotes and Delawares, too,
    As well as the tribe of Mingoe,
Invaded our land, and our citizens slew,
    On the South of the Ohio.

Andrew Lewis the leader and Charles the brave,
    With Mathews and Fleming also,
Collected an army, our country to save,
    On the banks of the Ohio.

With Christian, and Shelby, and Elliot and Paul,
    With Stuart, Arbuckle and Crow,
The soldiers one thousand and ninety in all,
    They marched to the Ohio.

These sons of mountain and valley renowned of old
    All volunteered freely to go
And conquer their foeman, like patriots bold,
    Or fall by the Ohio.

[LAST]

As Israel did mourn and her daughters did weep
    For Saul and his host at Gilboa,
We'll mourn Colonel Field and the heroes who sleep
    On the banks of the Ohio.

[1] In 1909 a monument eighty-six feet high and twenty-two feet square at the base was unveiled on the battle field of Point Pleasant. Andrew Lewis was a brigadier-general in the Revolutionary War. A statue of him and five other Virginians are grouped around the equestrian statue of Washington at Richmond, Va. Colonel Mathews was lieutenant-colonel in the Revolutionary War, and afterwards Governor of Georgia. Captain Shelby was first Governor of Kentucky.

REVOLUTIONARY SONGS

The American Revolution, viewed from its results, was one of the greatest movements in human history. The expenditures of life and treasure have often been exceeded, but the effect on the political life of the world is not easy to parallel. The chief result was the birth of the first successful federal government in history.

The keynote to the revolution was sounded by the brilliant young Boston lawyer James Otis, about 1764, when in a scathing address before the Superior Court against the issuing of writs by the Crown, he characterized the exercise of this power as an act which "cost one king of England his head and another his throne," and called upon the people to resist. John Adams who as a young man had heard this address made the comment fifty-six years later "then and there the child of independence was born." Patrick Henry of Virginia took up the cause with an eloquence never exceeded in this country, and in introducing a series of resolutions in the Virginia legislature in 1765, declaring that the people of the colony were entitled to all the privileges of natural-born English subjects, he thrilled his audience with that audacious passage, "Cæsar had his Brutus, Charles I his Cromwell and George III" — "Treason," shouted the speaker — "Treason," echoed other members — "George III" continued Henry determinedly "may profit by their example. If that be treason make the most of it." The resolution carried by a small majority and in time was broadcast throughout the press of the Colonies.

The Stamp Act Congress met in New York in October, 1765, with representatives from nine Colonies and expressions of moral support from the other four. It framed a Declaration of Rights which created the important precedent of colonial federation for mutual protection.

The Sons of Liberty organized in every colony to oppose the Stamp Act. "Taxation without representation is tyranny" became their slogan. Under the leadership of William Pitt, Earl of Chatham, Parliament repealed the Stamp Act but in the same session passed the Declarative Act declaring that Parliament had the right to tax the colonies in all cases whatsoever.

Under the latter act Townshend unwisely introduced the Acts of June, 1767, which bear his name, placing an import duty on tea, glass, paper, lead, *etc.*, thus precipitating the crystals of resistance in the Colonies. Immediately America was aflame again with the fire of revolution. The Virginian Resolutions of 1769 condemned the Townshend Acts and declared the people could only be taxed by their own representatives.

Regiments sent to Boston to enforce the law brought about the Boston Massacre in 1770. The armed British schooner *Gaspee* was burned in protest by citizens of Rhode Island in 1772 and the famous Boston Tea Party occurred in December, 1773.

All these events led up to the formation of the Continental Congress, at Philadelphia in 1774, and finally, after patience had ceased to be a virtue, the "embattled farmers"

> By the rude bridge that arched the flood
> Fired the shot heard round the world.

in Concord on April 19, 1775.

In spite of our familiarity with the foregoing facts, a review of them enables us to read with greater understanding the following songs of the times. We find in them, in consequence, a clearer reflection of the reaction to oppressive measures and finally to battle itself.

Early in January, 1778, David Bushnell, the inventor of the American torpedo, and other submarine machinery, prepared a number of "infernals," as the British termed them, and set them afloat in the Delaware River, a few miles above Philadelphia, in order to annoy the royal shipping which at that time lay off that place. These machines were constructed of kegs, charged with powder, and so arranged as to explode on coming in contact with anything floating along with the tide. On their appearance, the British seamen and troops became alarmed, and, manning the shipping and wharves, discharged their small arms and cannon at everything they could see floating in the river during the ebb tide. Upon this incident the following song was composed by Francis Hopkinson, a signer of the Declaration of Independence, a composer and musician of note, as well as having the honor of designing our national flag. It soon became popular with Washington's army, and is mentioned by Surgeon Thacher as follows: "Our drums and fifes afforded us a favorite music till evening, when we were delighted with the song composed by Mr. Hopkinson, 'The Battle of the Kegs,' sung in the best style by a number of gentlemen."

BATTLE OF THE KEGS[1]

Gallants attend, and hear a friend,
   Trill forth harmonious ditty,
Strange things I 'll tell, which late befell,
   In Philadelphia city.

'T was early day, as poets say,
   Just as the sun was rising,
A soldier stood, on a log of wood,
   And saw a thing surprising.

As in amaze he stood to gaze,
   The truth can't be denied, sir,
He spied a score of kegs or more,
   Come floating down the tide, sir.

A sailor, too, in jerkin blue,
   This strange appearance viewing,
First damn'd his eyes, in great surprise,
   Then said "Some mischief 's brewing.

"These kegs, I 'm told, the rebels hold,
   Packed up like pickled herring,
And they 're come down t'attack the town,
   In this new way of ferrying."

The soldier flew, the sailor too,
   And scared almost to death, sir,
Wore out their shoes to spread the news,
   And ran till out of breath, sir.

[1]Copied from "Songs and Ballads of the American Revolution" by Frank Moore, New York. D. Appleton & Co., 1856.

Now up and down, throughout the town,
 Most frantic scenes were acted;
And some ran here, and others there,
 Like men almost distracted.

Some fire cried, which some denied,
 But some said the earth had quakèd;
And girls and boys, with hideous noise,
 Ran through the streets half naked.

Sir William, he, snug as a flea,
 Lay all this time a snoring;
Nor dreamed of harm, as he lay warm,
 In bed with ——— ———.

Now in a fright, he starts upright,
 Awak'd by such a clatter;
He rubs his eyes, and boldly cries,
 "For God's sake, what's the matter?"

At his bedside, he then espied,
 Sir Erskine at command, sir,
Upon one foot he had one boot,
 And t' other in his hand, sir.

"Arise! arise," Sir Erskine cries,
 "The rebels — more's the pity —
Without a boat, are all afloat,
 And rang'd before the city.

"The motley crew, in vessels new,
 With Satan for their guide, sir,
Packed up in bags, or wooden kegs,
 Come driving down the tide, sir.

"Therefore prepare for bloody war;
 These kegs must all be routed,
Or surely we despis'd shall be,
 And British courage doubted."

The royal band, now ready stand,
   All ranged in dead array, sir,
With stomachs stout, to see it out,
   And make a bloody day, sir.

The cannons roar from shore to shore,
   The small arms make a rattle;
Since wars began, I 'm sure no man,
   Ere saw such a battle.

The rebel dales, the rebel vales,
   With rebel trees surrounded,
The distant woods, the hills and floods,
   With rebel echoes sounded.

The fish below swam to and fro,
   Attack'd from every quarter;
Why sure, thought they, the devil 's to pay,
   'Mongst folks above the water.

The kegs, 't is said, though strongly made
   Of rebel staves and hoops, sir,
Could not oppose their powerful foes,
   The conquering British troops, sir.

From morn till night, these men of might
   Display'd amazing courage;
And when the sun was fairly down,
   Retir'd to sup their porridge.

An hundred men, with each a pen,
   Or more, upon my word, sir,
It is most true would be too few
   Their valor to record, sir.

Such feats did they perform that day,
   Against those wicked kegs, sir,
That years to come, if they get home,
   They 'll make their boasts and brags, sir.

As a reflection of the hostility aroused by the Stamp Act, the Declarative Act and the Townshend Act, the following song, entitled "Fish and Tea," composed in 1775, is an interesting example.

FISH AND TEA

A new song to an old tune — *Derry Down*

What a court hath old England, of folly and sin,
   Spite of Chatham and Camden, Barre, Burke, Wilkes
     and Glynn !
Not content with the game act, they tax fish and tea,
   And America drench with hot water and tea.
     Derry down, down, hey, derry down.

Lord Sandwich he swears they are terrible cowards
   Who can't be made brave by the blood of the Howards,
And to prove there is truth in America's fears,
   He conjures Sir Peter's ghost 'fore the peers.
     Derry down, down, hey, derry down.

Now indeed if these poor people's nerves are so weak,
   How cruel it is their destruction to seek.
Dr. Johnson 's a proof, in the highest degree —
   His soul and his system were changed by tea.
     Derry down, down, hey, derry down.

But if the wise counsel of England doth think,
   They may be enslaved by the power of drink.
They've right to enforce it; but then, do you see,
   The Colonies too may refuse and be free.
     Derry down, down, hey, derry down.

There 's no knowing where this oppression may stop,
   Some say there 's no cure but a capital chop;
And that I believe 's each American's wish,
   Since you 've drenched them with Tea and deprived them
     of fish.
     Derry down, down, hey, derry down.

Ye birds of the air, and the fish of the sea,
  By the gods, for poor Dan Adams' use were made free,
Till a man with more power than old Moses could wish,
  Said, "Ye wretches, ye shan't touch a fowl or a fish!"
    Derry down, down, hey, derry down.

Three Generals,[1] their mandates have borne 'cross the sea,
  To deprive them of fish and to make 'em drink tea,
In turn, sure, these freemen will boldly agree,
  To give 'em a dance upon Liberty Tree.
    Derry down, down, hey, derry down.

Then Freedom's the word, both at home and abroad,
  And every scabbard that hide as good sword!
Our forefathers gave us the freedom in hand,
  And we'll die in defense of the right of the land.
    Derry down, down, hey, derry down.

Many songs supposed to have been in use during the Revolutionary War were actually written after the war. In this conflict between the Mother Country and her colonies, there remain very few war songs, especially in Maryland. The music of the period consisted chiefly of military marches. Strange to say, "Yankee Doodle" seemed to be the best known of the camp songs, and an interesting story is told of its survival (after much use by the fife and drum) during the Revolution in the festivities which accompanied the signing of the Treaty of Ghent. The Commissioners were told that their national anthem must be ready to be played by the band which would celebrate the English national anthem and the patriotic airs of the country which had been their home for months. Consternation reigned. There was no written music and none of the envoys were gifted. It was suggested that if they could whistle the air the bandmaster might catch it, but Adams, Bayard, Russell, all disclaimed such accomplishment. Finally, Henry Clay said: "I have it. My negro body servant, I know, can whistle anything." So he was brought in, performed "Yankee Doodle," the bandmaster caught it, and

[1] The three Generals were Burgoyne, Clinton and Howe.

saved the day. It might here be said that at the capitulation
of Cornwallis on that memorable day in October, 1781, the
English troops marched out to the tune of "The World Turned
Upside Down."

"Yankee Doodle" was written in England by an unknown
author, to an old tune of unknown origin, and is said to have been
sung by the much beplumed cavaliers in the time of Cromwell,
in derision of the latter's simple habits and attire. The tune is
supposed to have been written down and presented in fun, as
the recent martial music from Europe to the colonial soldiers
assembled to help General Braddock at Fort Niagara, by a
regimental surgeon, because their odd and uncouth attire re-
minded him of the impression made upon the cavaliers by Cromwell. The tune, which was already familiar in England as "Kitty
Fisher's Jig," became immediately popular in the army, and
about 1775 Edward Bangs wrote a series of verses to it, called
"The Yankee's Return from Camp." Since then almost innumer-
able verses have been put to it.

YANKEE DOODLE

Fath'r and I went down to camp,
    Along with Captain Good-'in,
And there we saw the men and boys
    As thick as has-ty pud-din'.

CHORUS

Yankee Doodle keep it up,
    Yankee Doodle dandy,
Mind the music and the step,
    And with the girls be handy.

And there we see a thousand men,
    As rich as Squire David;
And what they wasted ev'ry day,
    I wish it could be savèd.

CHORUS

And there was Captain Washington
Upon a slapping stallion,
A giving orders to his men;
I guess there was a million.

CHORUS

And then the feathers on his hat,
They looked so very fine, ah!
I wanted peskily to get
To give to my Jemima.

CHORUS

And there I see a swamping gun,
Large as a log of maple
Upon a mighty little cart;
A load for father's cattle.

CHORUS

And every time they fired it off,
It took a horn of powder;
It made a noise like father's gun,
Only a nation louder.

CHORUS

And there I see a little keg,
Its head all made of leather,
They knocked upon 't with little sticks,
To call the folks together.

CHORUS

And Cap'n Davis had a gun,
He kind o' clapt his hand on 't
And stuck a crooked stabbing-iron
Upon the little end on 't.

CHORUS

The troopers, too, would gallop up
  And fire right in our faces;
It scared me almost half to death
  To see them run such races.

CHORUS

It scared me so I hooked it off,
  Nor stopped, as I remember,
Nor turned about till I got home,
  Locked up in mother's chamber.

CHORUS

Naval war songs are represented by two long ballads — "The Yankee Man-of-War," author unknown, describing the daring bravery of John Paul Jones (born in Scotland in 1747 and died in 1792) in his cruise in the Irish Channel in 1778, and another anonymous song to the same hero, celebrating his victory on September 23, 1779, in the *Bon Homme Richard* over the British frigate *Serapis* and *Countess of Scarborough*, sloop of war.

THE YANKEE MAN-OF-WAR

'T is of a gallant Yankee ship that flew the stripes and stars,
And the whistling wind from the west Nor' west blew through the
    pitch-pine spars,
With her starboard tacks aboard, my boys, she hung upon the gale;
On an autumn night we raised the light on the old Head of Kinsale.

It was a clear and cloudless night, and the wind blew steady and strong,
As gaily over the sparkling deep our good ship bowled along;
With the foaming seas beneath her bow the fiery waves she spread,
And bending low her bosom of snow, she buried her lee cat-head.

There was no talk of short-ning sail by him who walked the poop
And under the press of her pond'ring jib, the boom bent like a hoop!
And the groaning water-ways told the strain that held her stout main
    tack,
But he only laughed as he glanced a-loft at a white and silv-ry track.

The mid tide meets in the channel waves that flow from shore to shore,
And the mist hung heavy upon the land from Featherstone to Dunmore,
And that sterling light in Tusker Rock where the old bell tolls each
    hour,
And the beacon light that shone so bright was quench'd on Waterford
    Tower.

The nightly robes our good ship wore were her three topsails set
Her spanker and her standing jib — the courses pulling fast;
"Now, lay aloft! my heroes bold, let not a moment pass!"
And royals and top-gallant sails were quickly on each mast.

What looms upon our starboard bow? What hangs upon the breeze?
'T is time our good ship hauled her wind abreast the old Saltee's,
For by her ponderous press of sail and by her consorts four
We saw our morning visitor was a British man-of-war.

Up spake our noble Captain then, as a shot ahead of us past —
"Haul snug your flowing courses! lay your topsail to the mast!"
Those Englishmen gave three loud hurrahs from the deck of their
    covered ark,
And we answered back by a solid broadside from the decks of our
    patriot bark.

"Out booms! out booms!" our skipper cried, "out booms and give her
    sheet,"
And the swiftest keel that was ever launched shot a-head of the British
    fleet,
And a-midst a thundering shower of shot with stun'sails hoisting away,
Down the North Channel Paul Jones did steer just at the break of day.

PAUL JONES' VICTORY

An American Frigate: a frigate of fame,
With guns mounting forty, *The Richard* by name,
Sailed to cruise in the channels of old England,
With a valiant commander, Paul Jones was his name.

CHORUS

Hurrah! Hurrah! Our country forever, Hurrah!

We had not cruised long, before he espies
A large forty-four, and a twenty like wise;
Well manned with bold seamen, well laid in with stores,
In consort to drive us from old England's shores.

CHORUS

About twelve at noon, Pearson came alongside,
With a loud speaking trumpet, "whence came you?" he cried:
"Return me an answer — I hailed you before,
Or if you do not, a broadside I'll pour." Hurrah!

Paul Jones then said to his men, every one,
"LET EVERY TRUE SEAMAN STAND·FIRM TO HIS GUN!
We'll receive a broadside from this bold Englishman,
And like true Yankee sailors, return it again." Hurrah!

The contest was bloody, both decks ran with gore,
And the sea seemed to blaze, while the cannon did roar,
"FIGHT ON, MY BRAVE BOYS," then Paul Jones he cried,
"And soon we will humble this bold Englishman's pride."
    Hurrah!

"Stand firm to your quarters — your duty don't shun,
The first one that shrinks, through the body I'll run,
Though their force is superior, yet they shall know,
What true, brave American seamen can do." Hurrah!

The battle rolled on, till bold Pearson cried:
"Have you yet struck your colors? then come alongside!"
But so far from thinking that the battle was won,
Brave Paul Jones replied, "I'VE NOT YET BEGUN!" Hurrah!

We fought them eight glasses, eight glasses so hot,
Till seventy bold seamen lay dead on the spot,
And ninety brave seamen lay stretched in their gore,
While the pieces of cannon most fiercely did roar.

Our gunner, in great fright to Captain Jones came,
"We gain water quite fast and our side's in a flame,"
Then Paul Jones said in the height of his pride,
"IF WE CANNOT DO BETTER, BOYS, SINK ALONGSIDE!"

The *Alliance* bore down, and the *Richard* did rake,
Which caused the bold hearts of our seamen to ache:
Our shot flew so hot that they could not stand us long,
And the undaunted Union of Britain came down.

To us they did strike and their colors hauled down;
The fame of Paul Jones to the world shall be known,
His name shall rank with the gallant and brave,
Who fought like a hero — OUR FREEDOM TO SAVE.

Now all valiant seamen where'er you may be,
Who hear of this combat that's fought on the sea,
May you all do like them, when called to do the same,
And your names be enrolled on the pages of fame.

Your country will boast of her sons that are brave,
And to you she will look from all dangers to save,
She'll call you dear sons, in her annals you'll shine,
And the brows of the brave shall green laurels entwine.

So now, my brave boys, have we taken a prize —
A large fourty-four and a twenty likewise!
Then God bless the mother whose doom is to weep
The loss of her sons in the ocean so deep.

POST REVOLUTIONARY SONGS

After a long seven years the war terminated with the treaty of November 30, 1782, though it was not until April 19, 1783, on the eighth anniversary of the battle of Lexington that General Washington proclaimed the war at an end, disbanded the army and retired as a private citizen to Mt. Vernon.

The aftermath of the war and the birth of the nation is reflected in "Hail Columbia," written by Professor Phyla of Philadelphia, who composed and played it at Trenton, New Jersey, when Washington marched to New York to be inaugurated in 1789. It was originally the "President's March." The words were written about ten years later, 1798, by Judge Joseph Hopkinson in Philadelphia. It was first sung by Gilbert Fox the year the words were written, Wednesday evening, April 25, 1798, and was published April 30, 1798.

HAIL, COLUMBIA

Judge Joseph Hopkinson

Hail, Columbia, Happy land!
Hail, ye heroes, heaven-born band!
Who fought and bled in freedom's cause,
Who fought and bled in freedom's cause,
And when the storm of war was gone
Enjoyed the peace your valor won!
Let independence be our boast,
Ever mindful what it cost;
Ever grateful for the prize,
Let its altar reach the skies!

CHORUS

Firm, united, let us be,
Rallying round our liberty;
As a band of brothers joined,
Peace and safety we shall find.

Immortal patriots! rise once more;
Defend your rights, defend your shore;
Let no rude foe with impious hand,
Let no rude foe with impious hand,
Invade the shrine where sacred lies,
Of toil and blood the well-earned prize!
While off'ring peace sincere and just,
In heaven we place a manly trust,
That truth and justice will prevail.
And every scheme of bondage fail.

CHORUS

Sound, sound the trump of fame,
Let Washington's great name
Ring through the world with loud applause!
Ring through the world with loud applause!
Let every clime to freedom dear
Listen with a joyful ear!
With equal skill and God-like power
He governed in the fearful hour
Of horrid war; or guides with ease
The happier times of honest peace.

Behold the Chief who now commands,
Once more to serve his country stands,
The rock on which the storm will beat;
The rock on which the storm will beat;
But armed in virtue, firm and true,
His hopes are fixed on heav'n and you.
When hope was sinking in dismay,
When gloom obscured Columbia's day,
His steady mind, from changes free,
Resolved on death or liberty.

CHORUS

Another song of the period was "Columbia," written by
Timothy Dwight (ancestor of President Dwight of Yale),
Chaplain in the Revolutionary Army. It was first printed as a
song with pianoforte accompaniment in the "American Musical
Miscellany" in 1789. It was also published in the *American
Museum*, Philadelphia, in June, 1787. (Earlier edition.)

COLUMBIA

Timothy Dwight

Columbia, Columbia, to glory arise
The queen of the world and the child of the skies
Thy genius commands thee; with rapture behold
While ages on ages thy splendors unfold,
Thy reign is the last and the noblest of time.
Most fruitful thy soil, most inviting thy clime
Let the crimes of the earth ne'er encrimson thy name
Be freedom and science and virtue and fame.

Thus as down a lone valley with cedars o'erspread
From war's dread confusion I pensively strayed
The gloom from the face of fair Heaven retired
The winds ceased to murmur, the thunders expired.

Perfumes as of Eden flowed sweetly along,
And a voice as of angels enchantingly sang
Columbia, Columbia, to glory arise
The queen of the world and the child of the skies.

The following lines, sent by the North Carolina Society, are taken from an old song called "The Battle of Kings Mountain," which was very popular in the Carolinas years after the Revolution. It was sung with applause at weddings, political meetings, and other gatherings where this ballad formed a large part of the entertainment." (Copied from Lossing's "Field Book of the American Revolution," Chapter xvi, p. 421.)

KINGS MOUNTAIN

We marched to Cowpens, Campbell was there —
Shelby, Cleaveland and Colonel Sevier,
Men of renown, Sir, like lions so bold,
Like lions undaunted ne'er to be controlled.
We set on our march that very same night;

Sometimes we were wrong, sometimes we were right.
Our hearts being run in true liberty's mold,
We valued not hunger, wet, weary, or cold.
On top of Kings Mountain the old rogue we found
And, like brave lions, his camp did surround;
Like lightning the flashes; like thunder the noise;
Our rifles struck the poor Tories with sudden surprise.

WAR SONGS OF 1812

CHAPTER II

WAR SONGS OF 1812

BENJAMIN FRANKLIN prophetically remarked that "the war ending with the surrender of Cornwallis was simply the war of Revolution, and that the war of Independence was yet to be fought." Twenty-two years after his death, the event was realized in the War of 1812.

The country had scarcely found itself, nor had it really won the recognition of the rest of the world. From a population of 1,600,000 in 1760 one-fourth of whom were slaves, it had increased in fifty years to a nation of about three and one-quarter millions, one-fifth of whom were slaves. The increase had been substantially free from immigration so that the homogeneity of the race was still intact. Nine-tenths of the people lived east of the Alleghenies. Kentucky and Ohio had been admitted to the Union now consisting of sixteen states. The Louisiana Purchase had added more territory than that of the original thirteen states, and "the winning of the West" had already begun. In maritime pursuits, the United States had prospered on account of the war between England and France, but when the empressment of alleged British subjects from service on American merchantmen was begun, which culminated in the attack of the *Leopard* on the U. S. Frigate *Chesapeake*, Franklin's prophecy was put in train for fulfilment.

Further blows at our rights and pride fell in the shape, firstly, of the famous Order in Council of January, 1807, whereby England closed by edict all ports under French control to neutral vessels that should not first touch at an English port and pay a duty. Secondly, came Napoleon's answer, the Milan Decree, declaring that any vessel having been searched or paid a tax at a British port might be seized as a lawful prize in any French harbor.

These two violations of international law forecast the War of 1812 which is remembered chiefly as a naval war. President Madison, a pacifist of the Jefferson School, after three years of "watchful waiting," was virtually forced by the "War Demo-crats" under the leadership of Clay and Calhoun to his declara-tion of war on June 18, 1812.

The country then, as recently, was ill prepared for war. Ten half-filled regiments were scattered about the western frontiers. The seacoast was unguarded. Our Navy consisted only of six first-class frigates and a dozen smaller vessels. Opposed to us was England's Navy of one thousand vessels, scattered, it is true, over the "seven seas" and at grips with France.

There is little satisfaction for an American to derive from the military campaigns. Michigan territory surrendered without a struggle. Fort Dearborn at Chicago was demolished by Indians. Queenstown Heights lost, in spite of the bravery of Col. Winfield Scott, and his later defeat at the bloody battle of Lundy's Lane marked the long list of failures by land up to 1814. Then followed the defeat of an American army of some six thousand men at Bladensburg in August of the same year and the humiliating capture and burning of Washington. Not until the glorious victory of General Jackson at New Orleans, heroically contested on both sides, did our land forces win a signal victory.

Little wonder is it then that the surviving war songs dwelt on our naval victories with the grand exception of our national anthem, "The Star Spangled Banner." A history of its inception has fortunately come down to us in the following letter from the pen of Chief Justice Taney, which was published in an edition of Key's poems in 1859.

(NOTE). The following Letter of Chief Justice Roger B. Taney gives the true history of "The Star Spangled Banner" as told to Judge Taney by the Author — Francis Scott Key himself. It was set to music — and published in "Hand Bill" form — with name of tune attached, Sept. 15th, 1814, by Judge Joseph Hopper Nicholson, on the same day that Francis Scott Key carried his verses to show Judge Nicholson, as Mr. Key states. This Letter of Judge Taney appears first as a Preface to "Key's Poems", and is as follows:

Addressed to Henry V. D. Johns, Lanvale Street, Baltimore.

My dear Sir:

I promised some time ago to give you an account of the incidents in the life of Mr. F. S. Key, which led him to write the "Star Spangled Banner" — and the circumstances under which it was written. The Song has become a National one, and will I think from its great merit, continue to be so, especially in Maryland; and everything that concerns its Author, must be a matter of interest to his children, and descendants; and I promised to fulfill my promise with the more pleasure, because while the Song shows his genius, and taste as a Poet, the incidents connected with it, and the circumstances under which it was written will show his character and his worth as a man.

The scene he describes and the warm spirit of patriotism which breathes in the Song were not the offspring of mere fancy or poetic imagination; he describes what he actually saw; and he tells us what he felt while witnessing the conflict, and what he felt when the battle was over, and the Victory won by his Countrymen. Every word came warm from his heart, and for that reason, even more than from its poetical merit; it never fails to find a response in the hearts of those who listen to it.

You will remember in 1814 — when the Song was written, Mr. Key resided in Georgetown, District of Columbia. You will also recollect that soon after the British troops retired from Washington, D. C., a squadron of the enemy's Ships made their way up the Potomac, and appeared before Alexandria, which was compelled to capitulate; and the squadron remained there some days, plundering the Town of Tobacco, and whatever else they wanted. It was rumoured and believed in Frederick, that a marching attack of same character would be made on Washington and Georgetown, before the Ships left the river. Mr. Key's family were still in Georgetown. He would not, indeed could not with honour leave the place while it was threatened by the enemy, for he was a Volunteer in the Light Artillery, commanded by Maj. Peter, which was composed of citizens of the District of Columbia, who had uniformed themselves, and offered their services to the Government, and who had been employed in active service from the time the British Fleet appeared in the Patuxent, preparatory to the movement upon Washington.

Mrs. Key refused to leave home while Mr. Key was thus daily exposed to danger. Believing as we did, that an attack would probably be made on Georgetown, we became very anxious about the situation of his family; for if the attack was made, Mr. Key would be with the troops engaged in the defense; and as it was impossible to foresee what would be the issue of the conflict, his family by remaining in Georgetown might be placed in great and useless peril. When I speak of us — I mean Mr. Key's father and Mother, and Mrs. Taney (his sister) and myself; but it was agreed among us that I should go to Georgetown and try and persuade Mrs. Key to come away with their children and stay with me, or with Mr. Key's father, until the danger was over. When I reached Georgetown, I found the English Ships still at Alexandria, and a body of Militia encamped in Washington, which had been assembled to defend the City; but it was believed from information received that no attack would be made by the enemy on Washington, or on Georgetown; and preparations were making on our part to annoy them by batteries on shore when they descended the river. The knowledge of these preparations probably hastened their departure, and the second or third day after my arrival the Ships were seen moving down the Potomac. On the evening of the day that the enemy disappeared, Mr. Richard West arrived at Mr. Key's house, and told him that after the British Army passed through Upper Marlborough on their return to their Ships, they had encamped some miles below the town and a detachment was sent back, which entered Dr. Beanes' home about midnight, compelled him to rise from his bed, and hurried him off, to the British Camp, hardly allowing him time to put his clothes on; that he was treated with great harshness and closely guarded. As soon as his friends were apprized of his situation, they hastened to the head-quarters of the English Army to secure his release, but it was peremptorily refused, and they were not even permitted to see him; and that he had been carried a prisoner on board the Fleet. Finding their own efforts unavailling, and alarmed for his safety, his friends in and about Upper Marlborough, thought it advisable that Mr. West should hasten to Georgetown and request Mr. Key to obtain the sanction of the Government to his (Mr. Key) going on Board the Admiral's Ship, under a Flag-of-Truce, and endeavor to procure the release of Dr. Beanes, before the Fleet sailed. It was then lying at the mouth of the Potomac, and its destination was not at that time known with any certainty. Dr. Beans as perhaps you know was the leading physician of Upper Marlbro' and an accomplished scholar and gentleman. He was highly respected by all who knew him; and was the family physician of Mr. West, and the intimate friend of Mr. Key. Dr. Beanes occupied one of the West houses in Upper Marlbro' and lived very handsomely; and his house was selected for the head-quarters of the Army, when the British troops encamped at Marlbro' — on their march to Washington. Their officers were of course furnished with every thing that the house could offer; and they in return treated him with much courtesy, and placed guards around his grounds and out-houses to prevent depredations by their troops; but on the return of the Army to their Ships, after the main body had passed through the town, stragglers who had left the ranks to plunder, or from some other motive, made their appearance from time to time, singly or in small squads; and Dr. Beans put himself at the head of a small body of citizens to pursue and make prisoners of them.

Information of this proceeding was by some means or other conveyed to the English Camp; and the detachment of which I have spoken was sent back to release prisoners and to seize Dr. Beanes. They did not seem to regard him, and certainly did not treat him as a prisoner of war.

Mr. Key readily agreed to undertake the mission in his favour, and the President promptly gave his sanction to it. Orders were immediately issued to the vessel usually employed as a cartel (The "Mindon") in the communication with the fleet in the Chesapeake; to be ready without delay; and Mr. John S. Skinner, who was agent for the Government, for "flags-of-truce" and exchange of prisoners, and who was widely known as such to the Officers of the Fleet, was directed to accompany Mr. Key; and as soon as the arrangements were made Mr. Key hastened to Baltimore where the vessel was, to embark, and Mrs. Key, and her children went with me to Frederick and thence to Mr. Key's father's home at "Pipe-Creek", where they remained until Mr. Key's return. We heard nothing from him until the enemy retreated from Baltimore, which as well as I now recollect was a week or ten days after he left us; and we were becoming uneasy about him, when to our great joy he made his appearance at my house, on his way to join his family. He told me that he found the British fleet at the mouth of the Potomac — preparing for the expedition against Baltimore. He said he was courteously received by Admiral Cochrane, and the officers of the Army as well as the Navy; but when he made known his business, his application was received so coldly, that he feared it would fail. General Ross and Admiral Cockburn who accompanied the expedition to Washington, particularly the latter, spoke of Dr. Beanes in very harsh terms, and seemed at first not disposed to release him. It happened, however, fortunately that Mr. Skinner carried letters from the wounded British officers, left at Bladensburg and in those letters to their friends on board the fleet, they all spoke of the humanity and kindness with which they had been treated, after they had fallen into our hands, by Dr. Beanes; and that after a good deal of conversation, and strong representations from Mr. Key as to the character and standing of Dr. Beanes, and of the deep interest which the community in which he (Dr. Beans) lived, took in his fate, General Ross said, that Dr. Beanes deserved much more punishment than he had received, but that he felt himself bound to make a return for the kindness which had been shown to his wounded officers, whom he had been compelled to leave at Bladensburg, and upon that ground and that only, he would release Dr. Beanes, but at the same time informed Mr. Key that neither he nor any one else would be permitted to leave the fleet for some days; and must be detained until the attack on Baltimore, which was then about to be made, was over; but he was assured that they would make him and Mr. Skinner as comfortable as possible while they detained them.

Admiral Cochrane, with whom they dined on the day of their arrival, apologized for not accommodating them on his own Ship, — saying that it was crowded already with officers of the Army; but that they would be well taken care of in the frigate "Surprise" commanded by his son, Sir Thomas Cochrane, and to this frigate they were accordingly transferred.

Mr. Key had an interview with Dr. Beanes before General Ross consented to release him. I do not recollect whether he was on board of the Admiral's Ship, or the "Surprise", but believe it was the former. He found him in the forward part of the Ship among the sailors and soldiers; he had not had a change of clothes from the time he was seized; was constantly treated with indignity by those around him, and no officer would speak to him. This harsh and humiliating treatment continued until he was placed on board the cartel (the "Mindon").

Dr. Beanes was a gentleman of untainted character and a nice sense of honour, and incapable of doing anything that could have justified such treatment. Mr. Key imputed the ill-usage he received to the influence of Admiral Cockburn, who it is still remembered, while he commanded the Chesapeake, carried on hostilities in a vindictive temper, assailing and plundering defenceless Villagers, or countenancing such proceedings by those under his command.

Mr. Key and Mr. Skinner continued on board of the "Surprise", where they were kindly treated by Sir Thomas Cochrane, until the fleet reached the Patapsco, and preparations were making for the landing of troops. Admiral Cochrane had shifted his flag — to the frigate, in order that he might be able to move further up the river and superintend in person the attack by water on the Fort. Mr. Key and Mr. Skinner were then sent on board their own vessel, with a guard of sailors or Marines to prevent them from landing. They were permitted to take Dr. Beanes with them, and they thought themselves fortunate in being anchored in a position which enabled them to see distinctly the flag of Fort McHenry from the deck of their vessel.

Mr. Key then proceeded with much animation to describe the scene on the night of the bombardment; he and Mr. Skinner remained on deck during the night, watching every shell from the moment it was fired, until it fell, listening with breathless interest to hear if an explosion followed. While the bombardment continued, it was sufficient proof that the Fort had not surrendered; but it suddenly ceased, some time before day, and as they had no Communication with any of the enemy's Ships, they did not know whether the Fort had surrendered, or the attack upon it been abandoned. They paced the deck for the residue of the night in painful suspense, watching with intense anxiety the return of day, and looking every few minutes at their watches to see how long they must wait for it; and as soon as it dawned, and before it was light enough to see objects at a distance, their glasses were turned to the Fort, uncertain whether they should see there the Stars and Stripes or the flag of the enemy. At length the light came and they saw that "our flag was still there", and as the day advanced, they discovered from the movements of the boats between the shore and the fleet, that the troops had been roughly handled, and that many wounded were carried to the Ships. At length he was informed that the attack on Baltimore had failed, and the British Army was re-embarking, and that he and Mr. Skinner and Dr. Beanes would be permitted to leave them, and go where they pleased, as soon as the troops were on Board and the Fleet ready to sail.

Mr. Key then told me that under the excitement of the time, he had written a Song — and handed me a printed copy of "The Star Spangled Banner". When I had read it, and expressed my admiration, I asked him how he found time in the scenes he had been passing through to compose such a Song. He said he commenced it on the deck of their vessel, in the fervor of the moment when he saw the enemy hastily retreating to their Ships, and looked at the Flag he had watched for so anxiously as the morning opened; that he had written some lines, or brief notes that would aid him in calling them to mind upon the back of a letter he happened to have in his pocket; and for some of the lines as he proceeded he was obliged to rely altogether on his memory; and that he finished it in the boat on his way to the shore, and wrote it out as it now stands at the Hotel on the night he reached Baltimore, and immediately after he arrived. He said the next morning he took it to Judge Joseph Hopper Nicholson to ask him what he thought of it; and he was so much pleased with it, that he immediately sent it to a printer and directed copies to be struck off in Hand Bill form; and that he (Mr. Key) believed it to have been favorably received by the Baltimore public.

Judge Nicholson and Mr. Key were nearly connected by marriage — Mrs. Key and Mrs. Nicholson were sisters.

The Judge was a man of cultivated taste; had at one time been distinguished among the leading men in Congress, and was at the period of which I am speaking, the Chief Justice of the Baltimore Court, and one of the Judges of the Court of Appeals of Maryland. Notwithstanding his judicial character which exempted him from military service, he accepted the Command of a Volunteer Company of Artillery, and when the enemy approached, and an attack on the Fort was expected, he and his company offered their services to the Government to assist in its defence. They were accepted and formed a part of the garrison during the Bombardment. The Judge had been relieved from duty and returned to his family only the night before Mr. Key showed him his Song, and you may easily imagine the feelings with which at such a moment, he read it and gave it to the public. It was no doubt, as Mr. Key modestly expressed it, favorably received.

In less than an hour after it was placed in the hands of the printer it was all over town, and hailed with enthusiasm, and took its place at once as a National Song."

I have made this account of "The Star Spangled Banner" longer than I intended, and find that I have introduced incidents and persons outside of the subject, I originally contemplated, but I have felt a melancholy pleasure in recalling events connected in any degree with the life of one with whom I was so long and so closely united in friendship and affection; and whom I so much admire for his brilliant genius, and loved for his many virtues. I am sure however, that neither you nor any of his children or descendants will think the account I have given too long.

With great regard dear Sir,

Your friend truly,

R. B. TANEY.

The composition of the Star Spangled Banner by Francis Scott Key was adapted to the tune "Anacreon in Heaven" by Judge Joseph Hopper Nicholson, who, as Captain Nicholson, fought the Battle of the Bombardment of Fort McHenry in 1814, Colonel Armistead, his superior, being ill in bed at home at the time.

Permission to use the original manuscript and the letter of Chief Justice Taney in this volume has been given by Mrs. Edward Shippen, formerly of 209 Monument Street, W., Baltimore, Md. (Rebecca Lloyd Nicholson Post Shippen, granddaughter of Judge Nicholson, and great niece of Francis Scott Key.) Mrs. Shippen is a member of the Maryland Society of Colonial Dames, having served as an officer of the Society between the years 1891 and 1898, and is now one of its Honorary Vice Presidents.

The "Star Spangled Banner" about which the anthem was written, was received by the United States National Museum first as a loan from Mr. Eben Appleton of New York City, the owner of the flag, in 1907. In a letter in 1912, Mr. Appleton formally presented the flag to the Museum.

The flag was owned by Colonel George Armistead, who so gallantly and successfully defended it, and descended to Eben Appleton, his grandson, through Mr. Appleton's mother, Georgiana Armistead Appleton, who was Colonel Armistead's daughter.

The "Star Spangled Banner" has never been officially adopted as our National Anthem, by act of Congress, but it is so recognized by the War Department, and all soldiers and sailors are ordered to stand at attention whenever it is played.

THE STAR SPANGLED BANNER
By Francis Scott Key

O say, can you see by the dawn's early light,
What so proudly we hailed at the twilight's last gleaming?
Whose broad stripes and bright stars through the perilous night,
On the ramparts we watched were so gallantly streaming;
And the rocket's red glare, the bombs bursting in air,
Gave proof through the night that our flag was still there.
O say, does the Star spangled banner yet wave
O'er the land of the free and the home of the brave?

On the shore dimly seen, through the mists of the deep,
Where the foe's haughty host in dread silence reposes,
What is that which the breeze, o'er the towering steep,
As it fitfully blows, half conceals, half discloses?
Now it catches the gleam of the morning's first beam,
In full glory reflected now shines on the stream.
T 'is the Star spangled banner! O long may it wave
O'er the land of the free and the home of the brave!

O say can you see ~~the~~ by the dawn's early light
What so proudly we hail'd at the twilight's last gleaming,
Whose broad stripes & bright stars through the perilous fight
O'er the ramparts we watch'd were so gallantly streaming?
And the rocket's red glare, the bomb bursting in air
Gave proof through the night that our flag was still there
O say does that star-spangled banner yet wave
O'er the land of the free & the home of the brave?

On the shore dimly seen through the mists of the deep,
Where the foe's haughty host in dread silence reposes
What is that which the breeze, o'er the towering steep,
As it fitfully blows, half conceals, half discloses?
Now it catches the gleam of the morning's first beam,
In full glory reflected now shines in the stream,
'Tis the star-spangled banner — O long may it wave
O'er the land of the free & the home of the brave!

And where is that band who so vauntingly swore,
That the havoc of war & the battle's confusion
A home & a Country should leave us no more?
~~Their blood~~
— Their blood has wash'd out their foul footsteps pollution
No refuge could save the hireling & slave
From the terror of flight or the gloom of the grave
And the star-spangled banner in triumph doth wave
O'er the land of the free & the home of the brave.

O thus be it ever when freemen shall stand
Between their lov'd home & the war's desolation!
Blest with vict'ry & peace may the heav'n rescued land
Praise the power that hath made & preserv'd us a nation
Then conquer we must when our cause it is just
And this be our motto — "In God is our trust,"
And the star-spangled banner in triumph shall wave
O'er the land of the free & the home of the brave.

REPRODUCTION OF THE ORIGINAL MANUSCRIPT OF
"THE STAR SPANGLED BANNER"

And where is that band who so vauntingly swore
That the havoc of war and the battle's confusion
A home and a country shall leave us no more?
Their blood has washed out their foul footsteps' pollution.
No refuge could save the hireling and slave,
From the terror of death and the gloom of the grave.
And the Star spangled banner in triumph shall wave
O'er the land of the free and the home of the brave!

O thus be it ever when freemen shall stand
Between their loved homes and the war's desolation;
Blest with vict'ry and peace, may the heaven-rescued land,
Praise the power that has made and preserved us a nation.
Then conquer we must, for our cause it is just.
And this be our motto: "In God is our trust."
And the Star spangled banner in triumph shall wave
O'er the land of the free and the home of the brave.

Commencing with the famous duel of August 19, 1812, between the *Constitution* and the *Guerriere*, which immortalized the name of Isaac Hull, American prestige rose to a high place on the seas. Commanding the *Wasp* against the *Frolic*, Capt. Jacob Jones won another duel in October off the coast of North Carolina. Within a week the frigate *United States*, commanded by Captain Decatur, captured the *Macedonian*, which was added to our fleet. The famous *Constitution*, *Old Ironsides* (now at Charlestown tied up at her last berth), under Captain Bainbridge, encountered and defeated the frigate *Java* off Brazil in December, and three hundred British merchant ships had been captured up to date by our privateers, mostly. We had, of course, suffered as well, but as Canning remarked in Parliament: "The sacred spell of the British Navy was broken."

Early in 1813 Lieut. James Lawrence of the *Hornet* met and destroyed the *Peacock* in West Indian waters, and in recognition of his success was placed in command of the *Chesapeake*. During the fatal attack by the *Shannon* were uttered his dying but immortal words, "Don't give up the ship!"

By the end of the year the English had captured seven American war vessels mounting 119 guns, while the Americans had captured twenty-six British war vessels mounting 560 guns.

Having sketched in the main the naval encounters celebrated in the War Songs of 1812, we cannot stop to pay the tributes deserved to Perry on Lake Erie, whose laconic despatch, "We have met the enemy and they are ours," stands graven on our minds with the heroic exhortation of Lawrence. Nor can we pause to laud the victory on Lake Champlain of the young MacDonough who has been pronounced "the greatest naval commander in America before the Civil War."

THE "HORNET," Or VICTORY

Rejoice! rejoice! Fredonia's sons rejoice,
And swell the loud trumpet in patriotic strain;
Your choice, your choice, fair freedom is your choice,
Then celebrate her triumphs on the main;
For the Trident of Neptune, long by Britain wielded,
At length to Fredonia reluctantly is yielded,
Then for Hull, Decatur, Jones, and for Bainbridge, swell
    the tones,
While the ready hand of fame
Bright emblazons ev'ry name!
Brave Lawrence, gallant Lawrence, now is shouting with
    acclaim:

CHORUS

Huzza! Huzza! Huzza! Huzza! Huzza! boys
Free is our soil and the ocean shall be free,
Our Tars shall Mars protect beneath our stars
And Fredonia's Eagle hover o'er the sea.

Attend! attend! ye gallant tars attend!
While your deeds are recounted in patriotic song;
Ascend! ascend! your banners high ascend,
And your cannon the loud chorus still prolong.
First the bold *Constitution*, led the path of glory,
The gallant little *Wasp*, then added to the story,
And a brighter glory waits
The renown'd *United States*,
For she gave Columbia's fleet
The new frigate that she beat,
While the fam'd *Constitution* sank another in the deep.

Again! again! Columbia's flag again,
Triumphantly floats where Britannia's used to soar,
In vain the main has own'd the *Peacock's* reign,
Her gaudy rainbow honors are no more.
She by Lawrence the *Hornet*, was so neatly basted,
A better roasted bird Johnny Bull never tasted;
Till she ended her career,
Like the *Java* and *Guerriere*;
For the *Hornet's* sting was ply'd
Till the sea with blushes dy'd
Its tyrant's fifth defeat in its bosom sought to hide.

Unite! unite! Columbia's sons unite,
And hurl on th' aggressors the tempest they provoke,
The fight is right, then raise your sabres bright,
And Britain soon shall tremble at the stroke,
The foe is on our coast! put your mountain-oaks in motion,
Fly to the main for our wrongs are on the ocean,
There is a flood of fire,
Ev'ry tar shall breathe his ire;
His motto, while he fights,
Be, "Free Trade and Sailor's Rights."
'Till even-handed Justice ev'ry injury requites.

THE "UNITED STATES" AND "MACEDONIAN"

How glows each patriot bosom that boasts a Yankee heart,
To emulate such glorious deeds and nobly take a part;
  When sailors with their thund'ring guns,
  Prove to the English, French, and Danes
  That Neptune's chosen fav'rite sons
      Are brave Yankee boys.

The twenty-fifth of October, that glorious, happy day,
When we, beyond all precedent, from Britons bore the sway, —
  'T was in the ship *United States*,
  Four and forty guns the rates,
  That she should rule, decreed the fates,
      And brave Yankee boys.

Decatur and his hardy tars were cruising on the deep,
When off the Western Islands they to and fro did sweep,
    The *Macedonian* they espied,
    "Huzza! bravo!" Decatur cried,
    "We'll humble Britain's boasted pride,
        My brave Yankee boys."

The decks were cleared, the hammocks stowed, the Boatswain
    pipes all hands,
The tompins out, the guns well sponged, the Captain now com-
    mands;
    The boys who for their country fight,
    Their words, "Free Trade and Sailor's Rights!"
    Three times they cheered with all their might,
        Those brave Yankee boys.

Now chain-shot, grape and langrage pierce through her oaken sides,
And many a gallant sailor's blood runs purpling in the tides;
    While death flew numbly o'er their decks,
    Some lost their legs, and some their necks,
    And Glory's wreath our ship bedecks,
        For brave Yankee boys.

My boys, the proud St. George's Cross, the Stripes above it wave
And busy are our gen'rous tars, the conquered foe to save,
    Our Captain cries, "Give me your hand,"
    Then of the ship who took command
        But brave Yankee boys?

Our enemy lost her mizzen, her main and fore-top-mast,
For ev'ry shot with death was winged, which slew her men so fast
    That they lost five to one in killed,
    And ten to one their blood was spilled,
    So Fate decreed and Heaven had willed,
        For brave Yankee boys.

Then homeward steered the captive ship, now safe in port she lies,
The old and young with rapture viewed our sailor's noble prize,
    Through seas of wine, their health we'll drink,
    And wish them sweet-hearts, friends, and chink,
    Who, 'fore they'd strike, will nobly sink.
        Our brave Yankee boys.

The Treaty of Peace, which has been described as "more remarkable for what it omitted than for what it contained," was signed December 24, 1814. "It was little else than a mutual agreement to stop the war, as both nations were tired of it."

The relief and thankfulness of the country was expressed in the following "Ode for the Return of Peace," by Lucius Manley Sargent, and sung in Boston on February 22, 1815, to the melody "Hail to the Chief." Sargent, who lived from 1786 to 1867, was an author and temperance advocate, a brother-in-law of Horace Binney, of Philadelphia, and himself a member of a well-known New England family.

ODE FOR THE RETURN OF PEACE

Written by Lucius Manley Sargent   Air: *Hail to the Chief*

Wreaths for the chieftain we honor, who planted
    The Olive of Peace in the soil that he gained.
Freemen his praise 'neath its shelter have chaunted;
    Secure in its branches, the ringdove remain'd.
        War blasts have scatter'd it,
        Rude hands have shatter'd it!
Flown is the nestler that tenanted there!
        Long from the pelting storm,
        None sought its blighted form,
Save that lone raven that shrieked in despair!

Hosannas, the high vault of heaven ascending,
    Hallow the day when our chieftain was born!
The Olive he planted, revives and is blending
    Its leaves with the laurel that blooms o'er his urn.
        Ne'er may the sacred tree
        Shorn of its verdure be;
Ne'er may the blast that hath scattered it blow.
        Heaven send it happy dew,
        Earth lend it sap anew,
Gaily to bourgeon and broadly to grow.

Sunk be the blaze of the bale-fire forever!
    Hush'd be the trump in the slumber of years;

Seraphs and Paeans of praise to the Giver,
Peace hath illumin'd a nation in tears!
May she in triumph reign,
Over our land again;
Ne'er may her fair floating banners be furl'd.
Still be the orphan's moan,
Silent the widow's groan,
Lost for a time in the joy of the world.

YANKEE THUNDERS

This song was written by L. M. Sargent, Esq. and sung at a dinner given by the Citizens of Boston to Captain Isaac Hull and the Officers of the Frigate Constitution, in honor of their victory over the British Frigate Guerriere. It was sung to the tune of "Ye Gentlemen of England" and the words of this song were taken from a fascinating little volume of old songs kindly loaned us by Miss Margaret Kendal Moore, Quaker Hill, Conn.

I

Britannia's gallant streamers
Float proudly o'er the tide,
And fairly wave Columbia's stripes,
In battle side by side.
And ne'er did bolder seamen meet,
Where ocean's surges pour,
O'er the tide, now they ride,
O'er the tide, now they ride,
O'er the tide, now they ride,
While the bell'wing thunders roar,
While the bell'wing thunders roar,
While the cannon's fire is flashing fast,
And the bell'wing thunders roar.

CHORUS

While the bell'wing thunders roar,
While the bell'wing thunders roar,
While the cannon's fire is flashing fast,
And the bell'wing thunders roar.

II

When Yankee meets the Briton, ·
Whose blood congenial flows,
By Heav'n created to be friends,
By fortune render'd foes
Hard then must be the battle fray,
Ere well the fight is o'er
Now they ride, side by side,
While the bell'wing thunders roar,
While the cannon's fire is flashing fast,
And the bell'wing thunders roar.

III

Still, still for noble England,
Bold Dacre's streamers fly
And, for Columbia, gallant Hull's,
As proudly and as high,
Now louder rings the battle din,
More thick the volumes pour
Still they ride, side by side,
While the bell'wing thunders roar,
While the cannon's fire is flashing fast,
And the bell'wing thunders roar.

IV

Why lulls Britannia's thunder,
That wak'd the wat'ry war?
Why stays the gallant Guerriere,
Whose streamer wav'd so fair!
That streamer drinks the ocean wave!
That warrier's fight is o'er!
Still they ride, side by side,
While Columbia's thunders roar,
While the cannon's fire is flashing fast,
And her Yankee thunders roar.

V

Hark 'tis the Briton's lee gun!
Ne'er bolder warrior kneel'd!

And ne'er to gallant mariners
Did braver seamen yield.
Proud be the sires, whose hardy boys,
Then fell, to fight no more;
With the brave, mid the wave,
When the cannon's thunders roar,
Their spirits then shall trim the blast,
And swell the thunder's roar.

VI

Vain were the cheers of Britons,
Their hearts did vainly swell,
Where virtue, skill and bravery,
With gallant Morris fell.
That heart, so well in battle tried,
Along the Moorish shore,
Again o'er the main,
When Columbia's thunders roar,
Shall prove its Yankee spirit true,
When Columbia's thunders roar.

VII

Hence be our floating bulwarks
Those oaks our mountains yield;
'Tis mighty heaven's plain decree —
Then take the wat'ry field ;
To ocean's farthest barrier then
Your whit'ning sail shall pour;
Safe they'll ride o'er the tide,
While Columbia's thunders roar,
While her cannon's fire is flashing fast,
And her Yankee thunders roar.

MEXICAN WAR: 1832–48

CHAPTER III

MEXICAN WAR: 1832 – 1848[1]

A HALF-DOZEN of the war songs of this collection owe their origin to the American colonization of Texas and the events surrounding the formation of the Republic of Texas in 1836.

In order to appreciate a number of the most frequent references in the songs it is necessary for us to recall a little of the early history of Texas.

In 1821 Mexico had finally succeeded in throwing off the Spanish yoke but had not effected any real settlement of Texas. In that year the United States had given up a claim to Texas arising from the Purchase of Louisiana, but Moses Austin nevertheless obtained permission to locate three hundred American families there. Upon his unexpected death his son Stephen carried out his plans and established a permanent Anglo-American settlement at San Felipé de Austin in December, 1821. During the following fifteen years some thirty thousand Americans filtered in along the rivers from San Antonio and Macogdoches to the coast. Remote from the real Mexico, they governed themselves without regard to the Mexican Government.

When, as a result of revolution, Santa Anna established his dictatorship in 1835, the Americans in Texas founded a permanent government, declaring in favor of the union with the Mexican liberals together with a restoration of the federal constitution of 1824. Santa Anna sent troops into Texas and war began. The desperate defense of the Alamo at San Antonio by 183 Texans under W. B. Travis in which the defenders were killed to a man, and the battle of San Jacinto in which Santa Anna was defeated and captured by a Texan army under Sam Houston were the outstanding events of the war. Practical independence resulted and between 1836 and 1845 Texas was an independent republic, a unique experience for one of the states of the Union.

The annexation of Texas in 1845 precipitated the Mexican

[1] We are indebted to Mrs. Edward Rotan of the Texas Society for much of the material presented in this chapter.

War and its cession to the United States together with California was confirmed by the treaty of Guadaloupe Hidalgo in 1848.

THE TEXAN'S SONG OF LIBERTY
William Barton

When the locusts of tyranny darkened our land
And our friends were reduced to a small Spartan band,
When the Alamo reeked with the blood of the brave
And Mexican faith slept in Goliad's grave,
When our star, that had risen so beauteously bright,
Seemed destined to set in thick darkness and night,
'T was then our proud leader addressed his brave men
And the prairies of Texas reëchoed — Amen.

"On, on, to the conflict, ye Texians brave,
March forward to victory or down to the grave!
Let your swords be unsheathed in liberty's cause,
And your bosoms be bared in defense of your laws!
Let your watchword be Fannin, in treachery slain,
And Alamo's sons, whose bones whiten the plain!

"For your friends and your homes let your rifle be aimed,
For your country that's bleeding, exhausted, and maimed;
Go, show to the world that our handful of braves,
Can never be conquered by myriads of slaves!"
'T was said, and the single starred banner waved high
O'er the head of our hero, whose deep slogan cry
Made the cravens of Mexico tremble and cower,
While our bugles rang forth, "Will you come to the bower?"

The Southwestern Historical Quarterly, which has collected and preserved many of these Texan poems, quotes, after "The Last Call for Assistance," the following note, evidently written by the owner of the original manuscript:

"Bolton and Barker in 'With the Makers of Texas,' p. 159, quote this poem, but omit the last stanza, which I give here as penned in the original copy in my possession. They reprint it from the *Telegraph and Texas Register*, August 9, 1836, where

the last stanza is also omitted. Drs. Bolton and Barker head it,
'The Texas Marseillaise.' The reader will note the words will
not accommodate themselves to that tune, however. My copy
reads to sing to the tune, 'Scots wha hae.' Drs. Bolton and Barker
state 'author unknown.' J. Freon was undoubtedly the author
in the absence of proof to the contrary. In my original manuscript copy he states 'written for Travis; The Last Call for Assistance.'"

LAST CALL FOR ASSISTANCE

J. FREON   Sung to the air: *Scots wha hae*

> Texians, to your banner fly,
> Texians, now your valor try,
> Listen to your country's cry;
>   Onward to the field.
>
> Armed in perfect panoply,
> Marshalled well our ranks must be;
> Strike the blow for liberty,
>   Make the tyrant yield.
>
> Who is he that fears his power?
> Who is he that dreads the hour?
> Who is he would basely cower?
>   Let him flee for life.
>
> Who is he that ready stands
> To fight for Texas and her lands?
> Him his country now commands,
>   Onward, to the strife.
>
> Small in number is our host;
> But our cause is nobly just;
> God of battles is our trust
>   In the dread affray.
>
> And when the war is o'er, we 'll see
> Texas safe and Texas free;
> Glorious will our triumph be
>   On each bloody day.

THE TEXIAN BANNER

By J. FREON, a Volunteer

O say, does the martyr-blest banner still show
Victorious the star of the Texian nation,
That shone so triumphantly out on the foe,
Like the sweet star of hope amidst extermination,
Where Jacinto's dread air was a breath and a snare
From the ghosts of Alamo and Goliad's pyre,
Its signal for freedom displaying abroad,
With vengeance and glory for man and for God?

O say, shall that banner e'er sink in the fight,
Beneath the dark mandate of annihilation,
While tyranny, trampling on all human right,
Shouts, "havoc and ruin are my exaltation"?
Oh, no, thou just God! with victory's rod
The hands of brave freemen thou lov'st to applaud,
Thou still will defend us and give us success
Till safety and peace our dear banner shall bless.

Come on then, ye freemen, to battle come on,
The free are returning and swear desolation;
They are mustering their bands, and in numbers alone
They trust, with a cruel and fierce expectation;
Let the free volunteer with his armor appear,
And force the oppressor to yield and to fear,
Then the sweet star of hope, like a heavenly isle,
On the banner of Texas with triumph shall smile.

THE TEXIAN WAR CRY

G. V. H. FORBES

As published in the *Telegraph and Texas Register* August, 30, 1836

Ye heirs of freedom! hear the war cry
  Now swelling from ten thousand tongues
In shouts betokening victory
  Blown o'er the world by trumpet lungs.
Awake! awake! the drum is pealing
  On Bexar's woody hills around;
  The tread of battle shakes the ground,
And rifles keen death shots are dealing.

Hurrah, hurrah, for war;
The battle flag waves high;
The rising of the Texian star
Shall light to victory!

Shall sons of Washington not rally
    When war dogs howl on yonder plain
And rapine stalks over hill and valley
    To bind us in oppression's chains,
Shall bigot violence and plunder
    On Brazon's banks infuriate roam
    And fill with fear each peaceful home?
No, answer with the cannon's thunder!

And by that blood-stained altar kneeling,
    The scathed and war torn Alamo
We pledge our all of patriot feeling
    To hurl red vengeance on the foe.
But now the tyrant's foot is crushing
    Each gray haired sire and blooming son
    Who lifts in freedom's cause the gun,
And shall not patriots dare his rushing?

Then, heirs of freedom! hear the war cry
    Now welling from ten thousand tongues
In shouts, betokening victory,
    Borne o'er the world by trumpet lungs.

The following bears the signature "S. A. M." It appeared
in the *Gloucester* (Mass.) *Telegraph* and seems to refer to the
Texas triumph over Santa Anna. *New York Mirror*, July 30, 1836.

TEXAS

S. A. M.

I hear them still; lo, where the footsteps thronging,
    Of armed thousands break upon the air,
And the tired sense is now for silence longing,
    Yet strains again the distant sounds to hear;

Lo, where unnumbered plumes are proudly waving,
    And helmets flittering in the sun's broad beam,
And the fierce war horse his proud hoofs is laving
    In the red blood that flows in many a stream,

'T is there the battle now is madly raging,
    And foe with foe maintains a fearful strife,
And the doomed hero, still the contest waging,
    Falls while he deems his own a charmed life.

Brave men and true, in freedom's cause unshaken,
    Yours was the task to make the cowards quail,
Yours the blest songs of liberty to waken,
    Till the loud echoes run through wood and vale.

Sing, for the conqueror's arm is now victorious,
    And war's shrill clarion hath not called in vain,
And freedom's banners now are floating glorious
    Above the field where sleep the early slain.

   The "Hymn of the Alamo" has a national reputation, and is
beloved by Texans. It was first published at Columbia, Texas,
in the *Telegraph and Texas Register*, Wednesday, October 5, 1836,
and signed "P."

HYMN OF THE ALAMO
R. M. POTTER

"Rise, man the wall, our clarion's blast
    Now sounds its final reveille;
This dawning morn must be the last
    Our fated band shall ever see.
To life, but not to hope, farewell!
    Yon trumpet's clang, and cannon's peal,
    And storming shout, and clash of steel,
Is ours, but not our country's knell!
Welcome the Spartan's death —
    'T is no despairing strife —
We fall! we die! but our expiring breath
    Is Freedom's breath of life!

"Here, on this new Thermopylae,
    Our monument shall tower on high,
And 'Alamo' hereafter be
    In bloodier fields, the battle cry."
Thus Travis from the rampart cried;
    And when his warriors saw the foe,
    Like whelming billows move below,
At once each dauntless heart replied,
"Welcome the Spartan's death —
    'T is no despairing strife —
We fall! We die! but our expiring breath
    Is Freedom's breath of life!"

They come — like autumn's leaves they fall,
    Yet, hordes on hordes, they onward rush;
With gory tramp, they mount the wall,
    Till numbers the defenders crush —
Till falls their flag when none remain!
    Well may the ruffians quake to tell
    How Travis and his hundred fell
Amid a thousand foemen slain!
They died the Spartan's death,
    But not in hopeless strife —
Like brothers died and their expiring breath
    Was Freedom's breath of life!

A number of miscellaneous songs appeared during the period covered by the Texas episodes, but without connection with them.

The most important of them was "America," which may only be included among the war songs because of its patriotic fervor, since it is not specifically of a warlike nature. The author, Samuel Francis Smith, D.D., a graduate of Harvard in the famous class of '29, was referred to as follows by Oliver Wendell Holmes in his poem "The Boys":

"And here is a nice fellow of excellent pith
    Fate tried to conceal him by naming him Smith;
    But he shouted a song for the brave and the free —
    Just read on his medal, 'My country of thee'"

In referring to "America," Dr. Smith wrote: "The song was written at Andover during my student life there, I think in the winter of 1831-32. It was first used publicly at a Sunday School celebration of July 4, 1832, in the Park Street Church, Boston. I had in my possession a quantity of German songbooks, from which I was selecting such music as pleased me, and finding 'God Save the King' I proceeded to give it the ring of American republican patriotism."

AMERICA

Written by SAMUEL FRANCIS SMITH   Air: *God Save the King*

My country, 't is of thee,
Sweet land of liberty,
    Of thee I sing;
Land where my fathers died;
Land of the Pilgrim's pride;
From ev'ry mountain side
    Let freedom ring.

My native country, thee,
Land of the noble free,
    Thy name I love;
I love thy rocks and rills,
Thy woods and templed hills;
My heart with rapture thrills,
    Like that above.

Let music swell the breeze,
And ring from all the trees,
    Sweet freedom's song;
Let mortal tongues awake,
Let all that breathe partake;
Let rocks their silence break,
    The sound prolong.

Our fathers' God ! to Thee,
Author of liberty,
    To Thee we sing;

Long may our land be bright
With freedom's holy light;
Protect us by Thy might,
Great God, our King.

Another song of this period which has long held its popularity
is "Columbia, the Gem of the Ocean." The author, Thomas
Becket, wrote in a letter to Rear Admiral Preble in 1876 that he
had written the song in Philadelphia in 1843, in which year he
had it published. Later, in England, it was sung and published
without authority as "Britannia, the Gem of the Ocean," and
on visiting London in 1847 he found it claimed as an English
composition.

COLUMBIA, THE GEM OF THE OCEAN
THOMAS BECKET

O, Columbia the gem of the ocean,
    The home of the brave and the free,
The shrine of each patriot's devotion,
    A world offers homage to thee.
Thy mandates make heroes assemble,
    When Liberty's form stands in view;
Thy banners make tyranny tremble,
    Three cheers for the Red, White and Blue.
    Three cheers for the Red, White and Blue.
    Three cheers for the Red, White and Blue.
Thy banners make tyranny tremble,
    Three cheers for the Red, White and Blue.

When war winged its wild desolation,
    And threatened the land to deform,
The ark then of freedom's foundation,
    Columbia, rode safe through the storm;
With her garlands of vict'ry around her,
    When so proudly she bore her brave crew,

With her flag proudly floating before her,
  Three cheers for the Red, White and Blue.
  Three cheers for the Red, White and Blue.
  Three cheers for the Red, White and Blue.
With her flag proudly floating before her,
  Three cheers for the Red, White and Blue.

"Old Glory" to greet now come hither,
  With eyes full of love to the brim;
May the wreathes of our heroes ne'er wither
  Nor a star of our banner grow dim;
May the service united ne'er sever,
  But they to our colors prove true,
The Army and Navy forever,
  Three cheers for the Red, White and Blue.
  Three cheers for the Red, White and Blue.
  Three cheers for the Red, White and Blue.
The Army and Navy forever,
  Three cheers for the Red, White and Blue.

Of great local as well as national significance is the following
song written by Judge William Gaston in 1848 and set to music
by Francis X. Hale.

THE OLD NORTH STATE
State anthem of North Carolina
JUDGE WILLIAM GASTON

Carolina, Carolina, Heaven's blessings attend her,
While we live we will cherish, protect and defend her,
Tho' the scorner may sneer and witlings defame her,
Yet our hearts swell with gladness, whenever we name her.

CHORUS

  Hurrah, hurrah, the Old North State forever.
  Hurrah, hurrah, the good Old North State.

Tho' she envies not others their merited glory,
Say whose name stands the foremost in Liberty's story,
Tho' too true to herself e'er to crouch to oppression,
Who can yield to just rule a more loyal submission?

Plain and artless her sons, but whose doors open faster
To the knock of the stranger or tale of disaster,
How like to the rudeness of their dear native mountains,
With rich ore in their bosoms and life in their fountains.

And her daughters the queen of the forest resembling,
So graceful, so constant, to gentlest breath trembling;
And true lightwood at heart, let the match be applied them
How they kindle in flame — Oh! none know but who 've tried them.

Then let all who love us, love the land that we live in,
As happy a region as on this side of heaven,
Where plenty and freedom, love and peace smile before us,
Raise aloud, raise together, the heart thrilling chorus.

During the Revolutionary War the defense of the Southwest
was entrusted to General Jackson. He found it necessary to seize
the Spanish town of Pensacola which had given assistance to the
British. After the war the Spaniards and Seminole Indians kept
up a harassing hostility against the inhabitants of Georgia and
Alabama. The purchase of Florida from Spain in 1821 failed to
put an end to this incipient warfare which broke out with the
Seminoles under Osceola in 1835 and lasted for seven years.

The "Soldiers' Song" by Thomas R. Whitney and dedicated
to Brig. Gen. Zachary Taylor and the officers of our gallant army
in Florida recalls a famous encounter of this war.

"Little has ever been known by our people of the numerous
instances of true bravery displayed by our troops in the Florida
war; and this ignorance has arisen from two causes: First, because
the war was conducted in a wilderness, beyond the immediate
view of the world; Second, because the character of the foe, and
the war itself (being waged only against Indians), deprived it of
that interest in the public mind which the event of war under
ordinary circumstances is calculated to inspire."

This song is a part of a longer poem published in 1845, "The
Ambuscade," intended to commemorate the battle of "O-kee-
cho-bee" or "Big Water." The battle was fought by Gen.

Zachary Taylor (then Colonel of the gallant Sixth Infantry), and the troops under his command, on the twenty-fifth of December, 1837, against a chosen body of Seminole Indians, far exceeding the whites in number and led by their chief, Halpatah Hahjo, the Furious Alligator; the Indians having first gathered their forces and chosen their position sent a challenge to the General to come out and fight them.

Wherever the incidents of this engagement are known, it must be regarded as one of the most signal instances of cool and intrepid bravery on record. Divested of all the "pomp and circumstance" of civilized warfare, and with no incentive to action save that of duty, the troops on this occasion bared their breasts to the volleys of the ambushed savage foe, charged upon his stronghold (wading waist-deep through a wide morass), and after a fierce struggle, obtained a victory over the concentrated forces of the Seminoles.

THE SOLDIERS' SONG

Thomas R. Whitney   Published 1845

Hark! 't is the early reveillé
    On the wildwood silence swelling;
Hark! 't is the soldier's song of glee,
    Of his bosom treasures telling.
His song is of those he 's left behind —
    Of honors yet before him;
And hope still flings, to cheer his mind,
    Her gorgeous mantle o'er him.

CHORUS

Huzza! huzza! to our friends afar,
We 'll join in the song of the sylvan war;
Our hearts are as light and our thoughts as free,
As the winds that sweep o'er the laughing lea.

Sweet, oh sweet, are the thoughts of home
    In warrior's breast abounding;
But hark! the fife and rolling drum,
    A call to arms are sounding.

And we must away, the strife is near,
    Every man to his duty;
Ours are the hearts that know not fear,
    Yet melt at the smile of Beauty.

CHORUS

Now, ere the shout of battle rings,
    Where thou and I may perish,
We 'll send a kiss on the zephyr's wings
    To the girls we love and cherish.
Our hearts they are there, our hands are here,
    And each with like devotion,
Must earn the field in *love* or *war*,
    Else never seek promotion.

CHORUS

Soon, soon we 'll end our wild campaign,
    And to our loved ones turning,
We 'll kiss them o'er and o'er again,
    Each heart with rapture burning.
And then we will swear no more to roam,
    From the laughing eyes of Beauty,
And keep our vows till rolling drums
    Shall sound the call "to duty."

CHORUS

CIVIL WAR SONGS

CHAPTER IV

CIVIL WAR SONGS

In the introductory letter of Gen. Theodore Ayrault Dodge to his son, prefacing his story of the Civil War, we find the sentiments that actuate us in the presentation of this chapter. "While holding the conviction that the cause of the North was right, I yield to no Southerner in my admiration of the splendid gallantry of our old enemy, now our brother, and I believe that no one will accuse me of intentional partiality in my narration of events."

In the songs included in this chapter will be found those like the noble "Battle Hymn of the Republic," free from rancor or reference to the enemy and expressive only of the loftiest patriotism. Others reflect the longing for homes, mothers and sweethearts, while a third type may more nearly be classified as "songs of hate."

War is bound to stir the entire gamut of human emotions, and their expression in song revives the spirit of the times in a peculiarly vivid manner, yet we are sure that the bitter sectional feelings are now safely at rest and happily quite past resurrection. Otherwise we should be loath to preserve the unbrotherly sentiments that necessarily must appear in anything like a complete selection of the songs that sprang out of the most tragic crisis of our national history.

The struggle that broke out in 1861 was the natural issue of the divergent views and practises of the North and the South regarding slavery, and the fulfilment of Lincoln's pronouncement of 1858, "I believe this government cannot endure permanently half-slave and half-free."

When the opposition of the North to the extension of slavery outran the endurance of the South, secession became the immediate *casus belli*, and it is around the themes of Freedom and Union that many of the war songs were written.

Eighteen of the thirty-three states were free states at the outbreak of hostilities, with a population over nineteen millions.

The Southern states counted about twelve millions, about one-fourth of whom were slaves. Hence the numerical odds against the South were about two to one. The homogeneity of the South was greater than that of the North, since immigrant labor had found neither an attraction nor a welcome to the slave-holding communities.

During the decade preceding the Civil War a steady stream of Easterners had been flowing into the western states. More than three hundred thousand settlers made their way into California in that time. Their places were filled by the foreign immigrants, but under these circumstances the rate of growth in the older states was less rapid. On the other hand in no slave state except Missouri and Texas was the increase much over one-fourth as great as that of New York. Such a condition only accentuates the temerity of the Southerners in putting their strength to the test against such odds — in a cause they felt to be just.

The conditions we have outlined and the sincerity of both parties to the conflict must be kept in mind by those who would peruse in an understanding mood the rival war songs.

The greatest heritage among these songs — and one which can now be shared alike by North and South — is "The Battle Hymn of the Republic." Julia Ward Howe, the author, was born in New York, May 27, 1819, and died in Middletown, R. I., October 17, 1910. Together with her husband she had edited the *Boston Commonwealth*, an able antislavery paper. In her later years she became prominent as a writer, a suffragist and an occasional preacher in the Unitarian churches.

The words of the "Battle Hymn of the Republic" were written by Mrs. Julia Ward Howe, under the following circumstances: In December, 1861, Doctor and Mrs. Howe, Rev. James Freeman Clark and Mrs. Clark, together with Governor John A. Andrew, of Massachusetts, visited Washington for a few days. McClellan's army was encamped near the capitol, and one day the party drove several miles out from the city to see a review of the troops. The review did not come off because, by an unexpected assault, the Confederates had surrounded a small body of Union soldiers, and the party saw reinforcements hurrying up to the rescue. This delayed the return of the party, and the roads were full of march-

ing troops, who sang army songs in which Mrs. Howe joined.
Among these songs was "John Brown's Body" which was sung
to the tune of an old Methodist hymn. Doctor Clark suggested
to Mrs. Howe that she should write some good words for "That
stirring tune." She applied her mind to the task and before dawn
the next morning she had produced the noble verses which have
been ever since wedded to a tune entirely unworthy of them,
though a good marching tune.

BATTLE HYMN OF THE REPUBLIC

JULIA WARD HOWE

Mine eyes have seen the glory of the coming of the Lord;
He is trampling out the vintage where the grapes of wrath are stored,
He hath loosed the fateful lightning of His terrible swift sword;
  His truth is marching on.

> CHORUS (after each stanza)
>
> Glory! Glory! Hallelujah!
> Glory! Glory! Hallelujah!
> Glory! Glory! Hallelujah!
> His truth goes marching on.

I have seen Him in the watch-fires of a hundred circling camps;
They have builded Him an altar in the evening dews and damps,
I have read His righteous sentence by the dim and flaring lamps;
  His day is marching on.

I have read a fiery gospel, writ in burnished rows of steel;
"As ye deal with my contemners, so with you my grace shall deal."
"Let the hero born of woman crush the serpent with his heel,"
  Since God is marching on.

He has sounded forth the trumpet that shall never call retreat;
He is sifting out the hearts of men before His judgment seat;
Oh be swift, my soul, to answer Him — be jubilant my feet!
  Our God is marching on.

In the beauty of the lilies Christ was born across the sea,
With a glory in his bosom that transfigures you and me,
As He died to make men holy, let us die to make men free,
  While God is marching on.

The tune adopted for the "Battle Hymn of the Republic" had been popularized by the song "John Brown's Body." Before coming to the latter we should, perhaps, refresh our minds with the incidents that made John Brown "an apostle and a hero" in the eyes of Victor Hugo, and the gallows on which he died "glorious like the cross" to Ralph Waldo Emerson.

John Brown, a descendant of Pilgrim stock, used to accompany his father as a cattle driver during the War of 1812. His experience witnessing the cruelty with which a slave boy of his own age was treated at a household where they once were staying had made an indelible impression on his youthful mind, which ripened into the intense hatred of slavery which incited him to the fatal and hopeless exploit that made him famous.

Late in 1859, having conceived an impractical plan to arouse the slaves to revolt, the gray haired man, followed only by his three sons and five colored men in a band comprising but nineteen men, took possession of the little arsenal at Harper's Ferry. After supplying his band with arms he sent six of his men, including one son, to search the county for slaves. A company of a hundred militia men was started to suppress the marauders about noon of the first day, followed in the evening by Col. Robert E. Lee with a body of marines and his aide, J. E. B. Stuart, later famous as a cavalry leader, when he was detached to demand surrender. Being refused, a swift engagement took place during which two of the Brown boys were killed and John Brown was severely bayonetted.

Nothing disturbed his intrepid spirit. Even after he had been captured and sentenced to death he wrote to a friend, "It is a great comfort to feel assured that I am permitted to die for a cause." To his wife he wrote, "My mind is very tranquil. I may say joyous"; and to his surviving children, "I feel just as content to die for God's eternal truth on the scaffold as any other way." His deportment up to the moment of his execution was as brave as his words.

Naturally the exploit stirred the country. The suggestion of a negro uprising and its frightful possibilities was good reason for the Southern alarm, while the heroism of this fanatical act kindled the abolitionist spirit to greater intensity.

There are several versions of "John Brown's Body," a song about whose origin there has been much discussion. Ednah Dean Proctor wrote a John Brown song but it was not popular. Dr. Louis Albert Banks says the song dates from 1861, when Massachusetts Volunteers on one of the islands in Boston Harbor amused themselves by adapting the words —

> John Brown's body lies a-mouldering in the grave,
>> His soul is marching on,
>> Glory, glory hallelujah,
>> His soul is marching on.

to a certain air. Numerous imitations in doggerel verse have also been made. Thane Miller of Cincinnati heard the melody in a colored Presbyterian Church in Charleston, S. C., about 1859, and soon after introduced it at a convention of Young Men's Christian Association in Albany, N. Y., but with different words.

"Professor James E. Greenleaf, organist of Harvard Church in Charlestown, Mass., found the music in the archives of that church, and fitted it to the first stanza of the present song," says Dr. Banks.

"Whatever may have been the origin of the melody, when fitted by Greenleaf to the first stanza of 'John Brown's Body,' it became so great a favorite with the Glee Club of the Boston Light Infantry that they asked Mr. Hall to write the additional stanzas."

GLORY HALLELUJAH!
OR
JOHN BROWN'S BODY
CHARLES SPRAGUE HALL

> John Brown's body lies a-mould'ring in the grave,
> John Brown's body lies a-mould'ring in the grave,
> John Brown's body lies a-mould'ring in the grave,
>> His soul is marching on!

CHORUS

Glory ! glory hallelujah !
Glory ! glory hallelujah !
Glory ! glory hallelujah !
    His soul is marching on.

He's gone to be a soldier in the army of the Lord !
    His soul is marching on.

John Brown's knapsack is strapped upon his back,
    His soul is marching on.

His pet lambs will meet him on the way,
    And they'll go marching on.

They 'll hang Jeff Davis on a sour apple tree,
    As they go marching on.

Now for the Union let 's give three rousing cheers,
    As we go marching on —
        Hip, Hip, Hip, Hip, hurrah !

JOHN BROWN
EDNAH DEAN PROCTOR

John Brown died on the scaffold for the slave !
Dark was the hour when we dug his hallowed grave ;
Now God avenges the life he gladly gave,
    Freedom reigns today !

CHORUS

Glory, glory hallelujah,
Glory, glory hallelujah,
Glory, glory hallelujah,
    Freedom reigns today !

John Brown sowed and the harvesters are we ;
    Honor to him who has made the bondsman free ;
Loved evermore shall our noble ruler be,
    Freedom reigns today !

John Brown's body lies mouldering in the grave;
Bright o'er the sod let the starry banner wave;
Lo! for the millions he periled all to save,
   Freedom reigns today!

John Brown lives, we are gaining on our foes,
Right shall be victor whatever may oppose;
Fresh, through the darkness, the wind of morning blows —
   Freedom reigns today!

John Brown's soul through the world is marching on;
Hail to the hour when oppression shall be gone;
All men will sing in the better day's dawn,
   Freedom reigns today!

John Brown dwells where the battle's strife is o'er;
Hate cannot harm him, nor sorrow stir him more;
Earth will remember the martyrdom he bore,
   Freedom reigns today!

John Brown's body lies mouldering in the grave;
John Brown lives in the triumphs of the brave;
John Brown's soul not a higher joy can crave,
   Freedom reigns today!

The two most prolific and popular writers of Northern War
Songs were George Frederick Root and Henry Clay Work.

Root was born at Sheffield, Mass., August 30, 1820, and died
at Bailey's Island, Me., August 6, 1896. Largely self-taught as
a musician he became an instructor of music at Boston from 1839–
44 and in New York 1844–45. He studied in Paris in 1850 and
afterwards was chiefly a composer. From 1859 he was a member
of the Chicago firm of music publishers, Root & Cady.

During the Civil War his noble patriotic music became of
national value and importance. His compositions became famous
incentives to enlistment, messengers of cheer in camp as well as
bracing the men to stand the shock of battle. In a catalog of
114 war songs, 36 are by his pen. The country owes him a debt
of gratitude which can never be repaid for his "Battle Cry of
Freedom," "Tramp, Tramp, Tramp, the Boys are Marching,"
"The Vacant Chair," "Just Before the Battle, Mother," "Just

After the Battle." They thrilled the souls of our people in mass meetings and in country school-houses; they made cheerful the lonely, tedious march and they fired the hearts of our soldiers with courage and enthusiasm, which carried them on to victory, time and time again.

"The Battle Cry of Freedom" was written in 1861 and was first given to the public in Chicago Court House Square, by the well-known Lombard Brothers, Jules and Frank. Soon after it was sung by the Hutchinson family at a public meeting held in Union Square, New York City, and became more popular than any other song during the heavy and hot contest of that conflict. It became the rallying song of the North, known by all soldiers and heard in all camps where the star spangled banner floated. In some divisions of the Northern army it was sung when going into action, by order of the commanding officers.

But Mr. Root not only succeeded in arousing the war spirit; he did as much toward rekindling the spirit of loyalty and bravery as the best speeches did, and he touched also the tenderest chords, those of home. "Just Before the Battle, Mother," "Just After the Battle," "The Vacant Chair," were, and still are, popular. They never fail to touch the veteran's heart; they never fail to cause tears to flow from the eyes of the aged mother, who offered her sons on their country's altar.

The John Church Company for many years held copyrights on the songs of George F. Root which have since expired and have been of great help to us in getting this and other Civil War material.

COLUMBIA'S CALL
GEORGE F. ROOT

O, come brothers all, 't is Columbia's earnest call,
    To make her people one again;
Let none stand aloof from the old paternal roof,
    Whose shelter ne'er is sought in vain;
Glorious the future rising o'er us,
    Blessed the era drawing nigh;
Then join heart and hand for the weal of fatherland,
    Where'er the starry banners fly.

Glorious the future rising o'er us,
  Blessed the era drawing nigh;
Then join heart and hand for the weal of fatherland,
  Where'er the starry banners fly.

O, dark was the day when we met in deadly fray,
  Dividing armies, friends, and fleets;
O, wild was the wail that rang out o'er hill and dale,
  As mourners went about the streets;
Now that the battle rage is over,
  Now that the minute guns are cold,
O, haste, knit again what the sword hath cleft in twain,
  Be friends and brothers as of old.

O, fair smiles the dawn, now the shades of night are gone,
  The dawning we have longed to see,
When truth shall prevail, and our joyful anthems hail,
  The glory of the brave and the free;
Come then, O North and South, united,
  Come, then, O East and West as one;
Rejoice in the light which has chased away the night,
  And heralds now the rising sun.

CAN THE SOLDIER FORGET?

George F. Root

Yes, beloved ones at home we remember
  And how can the soldier forget?
All the vows that were said when we parted
  Are sacred and dear to him yet.
When the night throws his mantle around us
  We dream 'neath the Heav'ns' starry dome
Of the dear ones whose sweet spell has bound us
  And whose voices shall welcome us home.

Yes beloved ones at home we remember
And how can the soldier forget?
All the vows that were said when we parted
Are sacred and dear to him yet.

Of the deeds that are hallowed in story
   We think as we pass on our way
And the pathway that leads us to glory
   Gleams brightly before us today
For the millions that wait on our efforts
   And myriads the future shall claim
When the pæans of vict'ry are sounding
   Shall most joyfully echo each name.

CHORUS

Oh hearts that in anguish are swelling,
   Ye eyes that are darkened with fear
For the brave ones ye loved past the telling,
   The fallen that sleep with us here.
They have burst now the fetters that bound them
   And high 'mid the heav'ns brightest ray,
E'en with glories immortal around them,
   They are looking upon us today.

CHORUS

THE BATTLE CRY OF FREEDOM

George F. Root

Yes we 'll rally round the flag, boys,
   We 'll rally once again
Shouting the Battle Cry of Freedom.
We will rally from the hillside,
   We 'll gather from the plain
Shouting the battle cry of freedom.

CHORUS

The Union forever, hurrah, boys, hurrah,
Down with the traitor and up with the stars
While we rally round the flag, boys,
Rally once again,
Shouting the Battle Cry of Freedom.

We are springing to the call
　Of our brothers gone before,
Shouting the Battle Cry of Freedom;
And we 'll fill the vacant ranks
　With a million freemen more,
Shouting the Battle Cry of Freedom.

CHORUS

We will welcome to our numbers
　The loyal, true and brave,
Shouting the Battle Cry of Freedom;
And altho' they may be poor,
　Not a man shall be a slave
Shouting the Battle Cry of Freedom.

So we 're springing to the call
　From the East and from the West,
Shouting the Battle Cry of Freedom;
And we 'll hurl the rebel crew
　From the land we love the best,
Shouting the Battle Cry of Freedom.

CHORUS

NATIONAL SONG
George F. Root

Come and join us with hearts and with voices
On this day when a Nation rejoices;
Tell again in the song and the story,
　With the bugle and trumpet and drum,
Of the fame and renown and the glory —
　Of the land that we claim as our own.

Tell the world how the right was defended,
How the struggle for freedom was ended,

How the tumult of war and commotion
   Found an echo far over the sea;
How the lands and the isles of the ocean
   Sent their sons to the home of the free.

May the future Columbia be glorious
Over wrong and oppression victorious;
May the star of thine empire ascending
   Guide the wanderer to freedom and rest;
May its light ever pure, never ending,
   By the whole world be honored and blest.

GOD BLESS OUR BRAVE YOUNG VOLUNTEERS
GEORGE F. ROOT

Hark the song of freedom, how it swells
   O'er valley, hill and prairie wide!
With thrilling tone the tocsin tells
   That dangers to our land betide;
And see from anvil, loom and plow,
   From home and mother's sacred tears
They fly with ardor on each brow.
   God bless our brave young volunteers.

Still, still the glorious numbers ring,
   And still they come our land to save!
Let every heart its tribute bring
   Of love and honor to the brave.
May He protect them in the strife
   Whose power can quell our rising fears.
Oh may He guard each precious life
   And bless our brave young volunteers.

Oh home of freedom, Fatherland,
   To Thee our treasure now we yield.
'T is duty calls — their feet must stand
   In tented camp, on bloody field.
Farewell true hearts, our prayers shall be
   Where'er the starry flag appears,
That He who made our fathers free
   May bless our brave young volunteers.

THE BUGLE CALL
George F. Root

Out from our homes and hearth-stones,
    Noble of heart and hand,
Each to the call responding
    "God and our own proud land."
Brothers and friends and husbands
    Follow the guiding star;
Gone from our homes, God help us!
    Gone, gone to the war.

Lips that are white with anguish
    Murmurs nor faltering know,
Saying a calm "God speed you,"
    Bidding them bravely go.
Somewhere the dangers are thickest,
    Somewhere it sounds afar.
All with our prayers and blessings
    Gone, gone to the war.

Oh if the Lord of battles
    Were not our strength and stay,
Mothers and wives and sisters
    Where should we turn today?
But knowing His power extendeth
    Where'er His children are,
Trusting we pray "God keep them";
    Gone, gone to the war.

JUST BEFORE THE BATTLE, MOTHER
George F. Root

Just before the battle, Mother,
    I am thinking most of you
While upon the field we're watching
    With the enemy in view.
Comrades brave are round me lying
    Filled with thoughts of home and God,
For well they know that on the morrow
    Some will sleep beneath the sod.

CHORUS

Farewell, Mother, you may never
    Press me to your heart again,
But O you 'll not forget me, Mother,
    If I'm numbered with the slain.

O, I long to see you, Mother,
    And the loving ones at home.
But I 'll never leave our banner
    Till in honor I can come.
Tell the traitors all around you
    That their cruel words we know
In every battle kill our soldiers
    By the help they give the foe.

CHORUS

Hark, I hear the bugles sounding,
    'T is the signal for the fight.
Now may God protect you, Mother,
    As He ever does the right.
Hear the "Battle Cry of Freedom"[1]
    How it swells upon the air.
O yes we'll rally round the standard
    Or we'll perish nobly there.

CHORUS

JUST AFTER THE BATTLE

GEORGE F. ROOT

Still upon the field of battle
    I am lying, Mother dear,
With my wounded comrades waiting
    For the morning to appear.
Many sleep to waken never
    In this world of strife and death,
And many more are faintly calling
    With their feeble, dying breath.

[1] In some divisions of the army the "Battle Cry" was sung when going into action by order of the Commanding Officer.

CHORUS

Mother dear, your boy is wounded,
  And the night is drear with pain.
But still I feel that I shall see you,
  And the dear old home again.

Oh, the first great charge was fearful
  And a thousand brave men fell.
Still amid the dreadful carnage,
  I was safe from shot and shell.
So amid the fatal shower
  I had nearly passed the day
When here the dreaded "minnie" struck me,
  And I sunk amid the fray.

CHORUS

Oh, the glorious cheer of triumph
  When the foeman turn'd and fled,
Leaving us the field of battle
  Strewn with dying and with dead.
Oh, the torture and the anguish
  That I could not follow on,
But here amid my fallen comrades
  I must wait till morning's dawn.

CHORUS

THE VACANT CHAIR

GEORGE F. ROOT

We shall meet but we shall miss him
  There will be one vacant chair.
We shall linger to caress him
  While we breathe our evening prayer.
When a year ago we gathered
  Joy was in his mild blue eye;
But a golden cord is severed
  And our hopes in ruin lie.

CHORUS

We shall meet but we shall miss him;
　　There will be one vacant chair;
We shall linger to caress him
　　While we breathe our evening prayer.

At our fireside sad and lonely
　　Often will the bosom swell
At remembrance of the story
　　How our noble Willie fell;
How he strove to bear our banner
　　Through the thickest of the fight
And uphold the country's honor
　　In the strength of manhood's might.

CHORUS

True they tell us wreaths of glory
　　Ever more will deck his brow;
But this soothes the anguish only
　　Sweeping o'er our heartstrings now.
"Sleep today! Oh early fallen,
　　In thy green and narrow bed;
Dirges from the pine and cypress
　　Mingle with the tears we shed."

CHORUS

THE FIRST GUN IS FIRED

GEORGE F. ROOT

The first gun is fired —
　　May God protect the right!
Let the free-born sons of the North arise
　　In power's avenging night.
Shall the glorious Union our fathers made
　　By ruthless hands be sundered
And we of freedom's sacred rights
　　By trait'rous foes be plundered?

CHORUS

Arise, arise, arise,
   And gird ye for the fight,
And let our watchword be
   "May God protect the Right."

The first gun is fired —
   May God protect the land!
And the bounding hearts of the patriot throng
   Now firmly take their stand.
We will bow no more to the tyrant few
   Who scorn our long forbearing,
But with Columbia's Stars and Stripes
   We'll quench their trait'rous daring.

CHORUS

The first gun is fired —
   Oh, heed the signal well!
And the thunder tone as it rolls along
   Shall sound oppression's knell.
For the arm of Freedom is mighty still
   Its strength shall fail us never —
That strength we 'll give to our righteous cause
   And our glorious land for ever.

CHORUS

TRAMP! TRAMP! TRAMP!
OR
The Prisoner's Hope

George F. Root

In the prison cell I sit
Thinking, Mother dear, of you,
And our bright and happy home so far away,
And the tears they fill my eyes
Spite of all that I can do,
Tho' I try to cheer my comrades and be gay.

CHORUS

Tramp, tramp, tramp, the boys are marching,
Cheer up, comrades, they will come,
And beneath the starry flag,
We shall breathe the air again,
Of the free-land in our own beloved home.

In the battle front we stood
When their fiercest charge they made,
And they swept us off a hundred men or more,
But before we reached their lines,
They were beaten back dismayed,
And we heard the cry of vict'ry o'er and o'er.

CHORUS

So within the prison cell,
We are waiting for the day
That shall come to open wide the iron door,
And the hollow eye grows bright,
And the poor heart almost gay,
As we think of seeing home and friends once more.

CHORUS

THE PRISONER FREE

GEORGE F. ROOT

Oh, the day it came at last
When the glorious tramp was heard,
And the boys came marching fifty thousand strong,
And we grasped each other's hands,
Tho' we uttered not a word
As the booming of our cannon rolled along.

CHORUS

On, on, on, the boys came marching
Like a grand majestic sea,
And they dashed away the guard from the heavy iron door,
And we stood beneath the starry banner free.

Oh, the feeblest heart grew strong,
And the most despondent sure,
When we heard the thrilling sound we loved so well,
For we knew that want and woe
We no longer should endure
When the hosts of freedom reached our prison-cell.

CHORUS

Oh, the war is over now
And we 're safe at home again
And the cause we starved and suffered for is won,
But we never can forget
'Mid our woe and 'mid our pain
How the glorious union men came tramping on.

CHORUS

Yes, yes, yes, the boys came marching, *etc.*

LAY ME DOWN AND SAVE THE FLAG

George F. Root

They arise, whose name was Legion
As an overwhelming wave
And the battle surged its billows
Round a chosen few and brave.
And they near'd the sacred banner
With their foul and flaunting rag
When the dying hero shouted
"Lay me down and save the Flag."

To the Siroc of Secession
They had bar'd the fearless brow,
They had heard *that* voice, and heeded,
Could they hear and heed it now?
But his heart is in the battle
Shall the hallowed ensign drag
While a hand is left to rescue?
"Lay me down and save the Flag."

Then they looked at one another
In the speechlessness of war
As each eye would ask a brother
Shall we stay or shall we go?
And again the sight was blasted
By the traitor boastful rag
And again the word fell sternly
"Lay me down and save the Flag."

Oh, beloved, ye who murmur
For the dear ones gone before,
For the manly son or brother
That may greet you never more,
For the loving arm that shielded,
For the hope whose pinions lag,
Let the lips that quiver, falter
"Lay me down and save the Flag."

STAND UP FOR UNCLE SAM!

George F. Root

Stand up for Uncle Sam my boys
  With hearts brave and true
Stand up for Uncle Sam my boys
  For he has stood by you!
He's made your home the brightest
  The sun e'er shone upon
For honor, right and freedom,
  He's many a battle won.

Oh, strike for Uncle Sam my boys
  For danger is near
Yes, strike for Uncle Sam my boys
  And all to you most dear.
Rebellious sons are plotting
  To lay the homestead low,
Their hands are madly lifted
  To give the fatal blow.

Oh, fall for Uncle Sam my boys,
   If need be to save.
Yes, fall for Uncle Sam my boys
   Though in a soldier's grave
His flag so long, our Glory
   Dishonor'd shall not be
But heavenward float forever
   The banner of the free.

WITHIN THE SOUND OF THE ENEMY'S GUNS
George F. Root

Within the sound of the enemy's guns
Within their sound are we.
A gallant band of patriot sons
Fighting the battles of Liberty
Beneath the folds of the flag of the free
      Boom ! boom !
Now, now ye Northern sons, rouse,
Rouse at the sound of the enemy's guns.
Yes, rouse ! Rouse ! at the sound of the enemy's guns.

Within the range of the enemy's guns
Within their range are we.
The parrott shell through the hot air hums
The Minnie shower from the thicket comes.
Stand firm ! Stand firm ! ye ranks of the free
      Boom ! boom !
Now, Columbia's sons, Charge !
Charge ! and take the enemy's guns
Yes, charge ! Charge ! and take the enemy's guns !

All silenced the roar of the enemy's guns
All silenced their lips — have we.
Awake the roll of the battle-drums
Raise high the cheer that surging comes
In the hour — in the hour of Victory !
      Boom ! boom !
Now, now, oh gallant ones Seize !
Seize ! for your trophies the enemy's guns
Yes, seize ! Seize ! for your trophies, the enemy's guns.

Though it is said that General Sherman's preference was Adjutant Byer's thought, "When Sherman Marched Down to the Sea," yet "Marching through Georgia" is the general favorite of the songs describing that famous historical event. Its author, Henry Clay Work, was born in Middletown, Conn., Oct. 1, 1832. He was of Scotch descent and his surname is thought to have come from a Scottish castle, "Auld Wark Upon the Tweed," famed in the days of the border wars. When he was quite young his people moved to Illinois. His boyhood was passed near Quincy in that state, and was one of abject poverty, for his father was taken from his family and imprisoned because of his strong anti-slavery views and activity in this cause. In 1845, however, he was pardoned on condition he left the state of Illinois. The family returned to Connecticut, and after a short attendance at school in Middletown, Henry was apprenticed to Elisha Greer, a Hartford printer. Like Franklin, he learned to write over the printer's case. Beyond a short term of instruction in a church singing school he had no musical education. A poetic temperament and a gift for music were his inheritance and many of his unambitious little poems found their way into the newspapers before he had finished his apprenticeship. His first song, "We're Coming, Sister Mary," written at Hartford and sold to George Christie, of Christie's Minstrels, was the beginning of his successful career as a song writer. In 1855 he went to Chicago, where he continued his trade as a printer. In 1856 he married Miss Sarah Parker of Hubbardston, Mass., and settled at Hyde Park. "Kingdom Coming," his first war song, was written in 1861; it was difficult to find a publisher for it, but once published its success was assured. Another slave song of his, which had a tremendous sale, was "Wake, Nicodemus."

Mr. Work realized a considerable fortune from his songs and after the war took an extended tour through Europe. While at sea he wrote a song, "The Ship That Never Returned," which became famous. Later he wrote two temperance songs, "Come Home, Father," and "King Bibbler's Army." He was an inventor as well as a song-writer and patented several machines.

On his return from Europe he invested largely in a fruit-growing enterprise in Vineland, N. J., but met with heavy financial losses.

His last years were saddened by his wife's insanity. He died suddenly in Hartford, Conn., June 8, 1884, and was buried in Spring Grove Cemetery of that city.

MARCHING THROUGH GEORGIA
HENRY CLAY WORK

Bring the good old bugle, boys! we 'll sing another song —
Sing it with a spirit that will start the world along —
Sing it as we used to sing it, fifty thousand strong.
  While we were marching through Georgia.

CHORUS

Hurrah, hurrah! we bring the jubilee!
Hurrah, hurrah! the flag that makes you free!
So we sang the chorus from Atlanta to the sea,
While we were marching through Georgia.

How the darkies shouted when they heard the joyful sound!
How the turkeys gobbled which our commissary found!
How the sweet potatoes even started from the ground,
  While we were marching through Georgia.

Yes, and there were Union men who wept with joyful tears
When they saw the honored flag they had not seen for years;
Hardly could they be restrained from breaking forth in cheers
  While we were marching through Georgia.

So we made a thoroughfare for Freedom and her train.
Sixty miles in latitude, three hundred to the main:
Treason fled before us, for resistance was in vain,
  While we were marching through Georgia.

BABYLON IS FALLEN
HENRY CLAY WORK

Don't you see the black clouds
Risin' ober yonder
Whar de Massa's old plantation am?
Nebber you be frightened, dem is only darkeys
Come to jine and fight for Uncle Sam.

CHORUS

Look out dar now
We 's agwine to shoot
Look out dar — don't you understand?
Babylon is fallen
Babylon is fallen
And we 's agwine to occupy the land.

Don't you see de lightnin'
Flashin' in de cane-brake
Like as if we gwine to hab a storm?
No, you is mistaken
'T is de darkeys' bey'nets
An' de buttons on dar uniform.

CHORUS

Way up in de corn-fields
Whar you hear de tunder
Dat is our old forty pounder gun.
When de shells are missin'
Den we load wid punkins
All the same to make de cowards run.

CHORUS

Massa was de kernel
In de rebel army
Ebber sence he went an' run away;
But his lubly darkeys
Dey has been awatchin'
And dey take him prisoner tudder day.

CHORUS

We will be de massa
He will be de sarvant —
Try him how he like it for a spell!
So we crack de butt'nutts,
So we take de kernel,
So de cannon carry back de shell.

CHORUS

"GRAFTED" INTO THE ARMY

Henry Clay Work

Our Jimmy has gone for to live in a tent;
　They have grafted him into the army.
He finally puckered up courage and went
　When they grafted him into the army.
I told them the child was too young, alas!
At the captain's forequarters they said he would pass —
They 'd train him up well in the infantry class.
　So they grafted him into the army.

CHORUS

　Oh, Jimmy, farewell!
　Your brothers fell
　Way down in Alabarmy.
　I tho't they would spare a lone widow's heir,
　But they grafted him into the army.

Drest up in his uniform, dear little chap,
　They grafted him into the army.
It seems but a day when he sot on my lap,
　But they grafted him into the army.
And these are the trousies he used to wear —
Them very same buttons—the patch and the tear;
But Uncle Sam gave him a bran new pair
　When they grafted him into the army.

CHORUS

Now in my provisions I see him reveal'd —
　They have grafted him into the army.
A picket beside the contended field,
　They have grafted him into the army.
He looks kinder sickish — begins to cry —
A big volunteer standing right in his eye.
Oh, what if the ducky should up and die
　Now they 've grafted him into the army?

CHORUS

UNCLE JOE'S "HAIL COLUMBIA"

HENRY CLAY WORK

Uncle Joe comes home a singin'
          Hail Columby!
Glorious times de Lord is bringin' —
          Now let me die.
Fling de chains into de ribber,
          Lay de burden by;
Dar is one who will delibber,
          Now let me die.

CHORUS

Ring de bells in eb'ry steeple,
Raise de Flag on high!
De Lord has come to save His people,
          Now let me die.

Bressed days I lib to see dem,
          Hail Columby!
I hab drawn a breff of freedom,
          Now let me die.
Ninety years I bore de burden,
          Den He heard my cry
Standin' on de banks ob Jordan,
          Now let me die.

CHORUS

Dis is what de war was brought for,
          Hail Columby!
Dis is what our fathers fought for,
          Now let me die.
Dars an end to all dis sorrow,
          Comin' by an' by
Prayin' for dat bressed morrow,
          Now let me die.

CHORUS

I hab seen de rebels beaten,
        Hail Columby!
I hab seen dar hosts retreatin',
        Now let me die.
O dis Union can't be broken,
        Dar 's no use to try;
No sech ting, de Lord has spoken,
        Now let me die.

CHORUS

I 'll go home a singin' Glory,
        Hail Columby!
Sence I heard dis bressed story,
        Now let me die.
'Tis de ransom ob de nation
        Drawin' now so nigh,
'Tis de day of full salvation,
        Now let me die.

CHORUS

SONG OF A THOUSAND YEARS

HENRY CLAY WORK

Lift up your eyes desponding freemen
    Fling to the winds your needless fears:
He who unfurled your beauteous banner
    Says it shall wave a thousand years.

CHORUS

A thousand years, my own Columbia,
    'T is the glad day so long foretold,
'T is the glad morn, whose early twilight,
    Washington saw in times of old.

What if the clouds one little moment
    Hide the blue sky where morn appears
When the bright sun that tints them crimson
    Rises to shine a thousand years.

Tell the great world these blessed tidings
  Yes, and be sure the bondman hears
Tell the oppressed of every nation
  Jubilee lasts a thousand years.

Envious foes beyond the ocean
  Little we heed your threatening sneers
Little will they — our children's children —
  When you are gone a thousand years.

Rebels at home go hide your faces
  Weep for your crimes with bitter tears.
You could not bind the blessed daylight
  Though you should strive a thousand years.

Back to your dens, ye secret traitors
  Down to your own degraded spheres
Ere the first blaze of dazzling sunshine
  Shortens your lives a thousand years.

Haste thee along, thou glorious noon-day,
  Oh, for the eyes of ancient seers,
Oh, for the faith of Him who reckons
  Each of His days a thousand years.

GOD SAVE THE NATION
HENRY CLAY WORK

Thou who ordainest, for the land's salvation,
Famine, and fire, and sword, and lamentation,
Now unto Thee we lift our supplication —
God save the nation!
God save the nation!

By the great sign, foretold of Thine Appearing,
Coming in clouds, while mortal man stand fearing,
Show us, amid this smoke of battle, clearing,
Thy chariot nearing!
Thy chariot nearing!

By the brave blood that floweth like a river,
Hurl Thou a thunderbolt from out Thy quiver!
Break Thou the strong gates! ev'ry fetter shiver!
Smite and deliver!
Smite and deliver!

Slay Thou our foes, or turn them to derision —
Till through the blood-red Valley of Decision,
Peace on our fields shine, like a prophet's vision.
Green and elysian!
Green and elysian!

WHEN SHERMAN MARCHED DOWN TO THE SEA

HENRY CLAY WORK

Our campfires shone bright on the mountain
    That frowned on the river below,
While we stood by our guns in the morning
    And eagerly watched the foe.
When a horseman rode out in the darkness
    That hung over mountain and tree
And shouted, "Boys, up and be ready,
    For Sherman will march to the sea."

When cheer upon cheer for bold Sherman
    Went up from each valley and glen
And the bugles reëchoed the music
    That came from the lips of the men.
For we knew that the stars on our banners
    More bright in their splendor would be
And the blessings of Northland would greet us
    When Sherman marched down to the sea.

Then forward boys, forward to battle
    We marched on our wearisome way
And we stormed the wild hills of Resaca
    God bless those who fell on that day.
Then Kennesaw dark in its glory,
    Frown'd down on the flag of the free,
But the East and the West bore her standard
    When Sherman marched down to the sea.

Still onward we pressed 'til our banners
  Swept out from Atlanta's grim walls,
And the blood of the patriot dampened
  The soil where the traitors' flag falls.
But we paused not to weep for the fallen
  Who slept by each river and tree.
Yet we twined them a wreath of the laurel
  And Sherman marched down to the sea.

Proud, proud was our Army that morning
  That stood by the cypress and pine.
Then Sherman said: "Boys, you are weary,
  This day fair Savannah is mine."
Then sang we a song to our Chieftain
  That echoed o'er river and sea;
And the stars on our banners shone brighter
  When Sherman marched down to the sea.

WHEN OUR BOYS COME HOME

Henry Clay Work

When our boys come home in triumph
  With the laurels they shall gain,
When we go to give them welcome, brother,
  We shall look for you in vain.
We shall wait for your returning, brother,
  Tho' we know it cannot be;
For your comrades left you sleeping, brother,
  Underneath a southern tree.

REFRAIN

Sleeping to waken in this weary world no more
  Sleeping for your true lov'd country, brother,
Sleeping for the flag you bore.

You who were the first on duty, brother,
  When "to arms" your leader cried,
You have left the ranks forever, brother,
  You have laid your arms aside.

From the awful scenes of battle, brother,
    You were set forever free
When your comrades left you sleeping, brother,
    Underneath the southern tree.

REFRAIN

You have crossed the clouded river, brother,
    To the mansions of the blest.
Where the wicked cease from troubling, brother,
    And the weary are at rest.
Surely we would not recall you, brother,
    But the tears flow fast and free,
When we think of you as sleeping, brother,
    Underneath that southern tree.

REFRAIN

COLUMBIA'S GUARDIAN ANGELS

HENRY CLAY WORK

An echo floats down from the mountains
    And finds on the prairies release
An echo whose wonderful burden
    Is "Victory, Liberty, Peace."

REFRAIN

The glorious trio, behold they are coming
    Their heralds are standing e'en now.
Go tell the lone watchers of earth they are coming
    To bless us — be with us — forsake us no more.

CHORUS

"Glory to God in the Highest"
    And the people shall answer "Amen"
Columbia's Guardian Angels
    Return to their empire again.

The banner hangs high in the heavens,
　The beacon commences to burn,
The shout of the freedmen goes upward
　To welcome their waited return.

REFRAIN AND CHORUS

The stronghold of tyranny trembles
　The minions retire in dismay
Like specters that fade in the darkness
　Before the arrival of day.

REFRAIN AND CHORUS

They bring us the place among nations
　Our ancestors gave us before
The birthright that some would have bartered
　They now in its fulness restore.

REFRAIN AND CHORUS

They bring us that blessing of blessings,
　Which few were yet looking to see,
A firm and unchangeable Union
　In fact, as in theory, free.

REFRAIN AND CHORUS

KINGDOM COMING

Henry Clay Work

Say darkeys hab you seen de massa,
　Wid de mufftash on his face,
Go long de road some time dis mornin'
　Like he gwine to leab de place?

He seen a smoke way up de ribber
　Whar de Linkum gun-boats lay;
He took his hat an' lef berry sudden
　An' I spec he 's run away!

CHORUS

De massa run ? Ha ! ha !
    De massa run ? Ho ! ho !
It must be now de kingdom comin'
    An' de year ob Jubilo !

He six feet one way, two feet tudder
    An' weigh tree hundred pound;
His coat so big he could n't pay de tailor,
    An' it won't go half way 'round.
He drill so much dey call him captain,
    An' he get so drefful tann'd,
I spec he try an' fool dem Yankees
    For to think he 's contraband.

CHORUS

De darkeys feel so lonesome
    Libing in de log-house in de lawn,
Dey move dar tings to massa's parlor
    For to keep it while he gone.
Dar 's wine an' cider in de kitchen,
    An' de darkeys dey 'll hab some;
I spec dey 'll all be confiscated
    When de Linkum sogers come.

CHORUS

De oberseer he make us trouble
    An' he dribe us 'round a spell;
We lock him up in de smokehouse cellar
    Wid de key trown in de well.
De whip is lost, de han'cuff broken,
    But de massa 'll hab his pay;
He 's ole enough, big enough
Ought to known better
    Den to went an' run away.

CHORUS

WAKE NICODEMUS

Henry Clay Work

Nicodemus the slave was of African birth
　And was bought for a bagful of gold.
He was reckoned as part of the salt of the earth,
　But he died years ago very old.
'T was his last sad request, as we laid him away;
　In the trunk of an old hollow tree.
"Wake me up," was his charge, "At the first break of day,
　Wake me up for the great Jubilee."

CHORUS

　　　The good time coming is almost here —
　　　　It was long, long, long, on the way;
　　　Now run an' tell Elijah to hurry up Pomp
　　　An' meet us at the gum-tree down by the swamp
　　　　To wake Nicodemus today.

He was known as a prophet, — at least was as wise —
　For he told of the battles to come,
And we trembled with dread when he rolled up his eyes,
　And we heeded the shake of his thumb.
Tho' he clothed us with fear, yet the garments he wore
　Were in patches at elbow and knee,
And he still wears his suit that he used to of yore
　And he sleeps in the old hollow tree.

CHORUS

Nicodemus was never the sport of the lash
　Tho' the bullet has oft crossed his path.
There were none of his masters so brave or so rash
　As to face such a man in his wrath.
Yet his great heart with kindness was filled to the brim;
　He obeyed, who was born to command;
But he longed for the morning which then was so dim,
　For the morning which is now at hand.

CHORUS

'T was a long weary night — we were almost in fear
  That the future was more than he knew.
'T was a long weary night — but the morning is near
  And the words of our prophet are true.
There are signs in the sky that the darkness is gone,
  There are tokens in endless array,
While the storm which had seemingly banished the dawn
  Only hastens the advent of day.

CHORUS

OUR CAPTAIN'S LAST WORDS
HENRY CLAY WORK

Where the foremost flag was flying
  Pierced by many a shot and shell,
Where the bravest men were dying,
  There our gallant captain fell.
"Boys! you follow now another,
  Follow till the foe shall yield."
Then, he whispered, "Tell my mother
  Stephen died upon the field.
  Mother, mother, Stephen died upon the field."

Thro' the battle smoke they bore him,
  But his words were growing wild;
Heeding not the scenes before him,
  Stephen was once more a child.
"Ah, she comes, there is no other
  Speaks my name with such a joy.
Press me to your bosom, mother,
  Call me still your darling boy.
  Mother, mother, call me still your darling boy."

Men who were not used to weeping
  Turn'd aside to hide a tear
When they saw the pallor creeping
  That assured them Death was near.
Kindly as he were a brother
  Strangers caught his parting breath
Laden with the murmur, "Mother"
  Last upon his lips in death.
  "Mother, mother," last upon his lips in death.

GOD SAVE THE PRESIDENT
Published in the *Bugle Call*

God save the President!
His chosen instrument
   May Heaven bless.
God give him while he bears
The weight of public cares
And asks the people's Prayers,
   A good success.

God bless the honest man
Who leads the Union van
   In peril's hour.
While rebels' tempests rail
And storms the State assail
God give him to prevail
   By heavenly power.

And when the war is won,
May he like Washington
   Deliv'rer prove
And Father Abraham be
Our Pater Patriæ
Whom Sire of Liberty
   The people love.

Let all with might and main
Our chosen chief sustain —
   Prudent and brave,
Strong in upright intent,
Nor from his purpose bent —
God save the President!
   The Union save.

'T IS FINISHED, 'T IS ENDED
Words and Music by HENRY C. WORK

'T is finished, 't is ended,
   The dreadful, awful task is done;
The wounded and bleeding,
   'T is ours to sing the vict'ry won.

Our nation is ransomed,
   Our enemies are overthrown,
And now, now commences
   The brightest era ever known.

CHORUS

Then sing Hallelujah,
   Glory be to God on High,
For the old flag with the white flag
   Is hanging in the azure sky.

Ye joy bells, ye peace bells,
   Oh never, never music rang
So sweetly, so grandly,
   Since angels in the Advent sang.
Your message is gladness
   To myriads of waiting souls,
As onward and worldward
   The happy, happy echo rolls.

CHORUS

Come patriots, come freemen,
   Come join your every heart and voice;
We 've wept with the weeping,
   Now let us with the blest rejoice —
With armies of victors
   Who round about the white throne stand
With Lincoln, the Martyr
   And Liberator of his land.

CHORUS

A BATTLE HYMN

Music by WORK   Words by THEO. TILTON

Thou who ordainest for the land's salvation
Famine and fire and sword and lamentation,
Now unto Thee we lift our supplication,
God save the Nation, God save the Nation.

By the great sign foretold of thine appearing,
Coming in clouds while mortal man stands fearing,
Show us amid this smoke of battle clearing
Thy chariot nearing, Thy chariot nearing.

By the brave blood that floweth like a river
Hurl Thou a thunderbolt from out Thy quiver;
Break Thou the strong gates, ev'ry fetter shiver
Smite and deliver, Smite and deliver.

Slay Thou our foes or turn them to derision,
Till through the blood red valley of Decision
Peace on our fields shine, like a prophet's vision
Green and Elysian, Green and Elysian.

"Tenting on the Old Camp Ground" was written by Walter Kittredge, who was born in Merrimac, N. H., October 8, 1832. He was educated at the village school and, like many other writers of war songs, Kittredge had an ear for music. All his knowledge of music, however, was picked up by himself, never having had a teacher. "Tenting on the Old Camp Ground," more than any other of our American War Songs, had in it the heart experience of the man who wrote it. In 1863 Kittredge was drafted into the army. That night in bed he was the prey of conflicting emotions, being loyal to his country, but revolting against war. In the middle of the night he awoke with dread and suddenly the verses began to form in his mind. The first verse reveals his purpose not only to give cheer to others, but to comfort his own heart.

Being a musician, a tune for the song easily came to Kittredge's mind, and after copying both words and music, he went at once to Lynn, Mass., to visit his friend, Asa Hutchinson, one of the famous Hutchinson family who then lived at Bird's Nest Cottage, at High Rock. After they had looked it over together they called in John Hutchinson to sing the solo. Asa Hutchinson sang the bass, and the children joined in the chorus. Kittredge at once made a contract with Asa Hutchinson to arrange the song properly and publish it for one-half the profits.

The Hutchinson family were just then giving a series of torchlight concerts on the crest of old High Rock, with the tickets at the exceedingly popular price of five cents. During the day they would wind balls of old cloth and soak them in oils. These, placed in pans on the tops of posts at intervals, would burn steadily for an hour or more, and boys stood ready to replace them when they burned out. The audience gathered in thousands every night during this remarkable series of concerts, and on the very night of the day Kittredge had brought his new hymn, "Tenting on the Old Camp Ground" was sung for the first time from the crest of High Rock.

Dr. Banks' estimate of the song is largely sentimental, but while it has always been a great favorite, the military students are warned against tenting on an old camp ground. The old camp ground was said to be beautiful from a poetic standpoint, but exactly the opposite from the point of view of sanitation.

While copyrights on the Civil War Songs have practically run out, Oliver Ditson & Company have been most kind in helping us get material and have given us permission on many of these songs, of which this is one.

TENTING ON THE OLD CAMP GROUND

WALTER KITTREDGE

We 're tenting tonight on the old camp ground;
    Give us a song to cheer
Our weary hearts, a song of home,
    And friends we love so dear.

CHORUS

Many are the hearts that are weary tonight,
    Wishing for the war to cease;
Many are the hearts, looking for the right,
    To see the dawn of peace.
Tenting tonight, tenting tonight,
    Tenting on the old camp ground.

We 've been tenting tonight on the old camp ground,
    Thinking of the days gone by,
Of the loved ones at home, that gave us the hand,
    And the tear that said "Good-by!"

CHORUS

We are tired of war on the old camp ground,
  Many are dead and gone,
Of the brave and true who 've left their homes,
  Others been wounded long.

CHORUS

We 've been fighting today on the old camp ground,
  Many are lying near;
Some are dead and some are dying,
  Many are in tears.

REFRAIN

Many are the hearts that are weary tonight,
  Wishing for the war to cease,
Many are the hearts, looking for the right,
  To see the dawn of peace.
Dying tonight, dying tonight,
  Dying on the old camp ground.

SHERIDAN'S RIDE

THOMAS BUCHANAN READ

Thomas Buchanan Read, American poet and painter, was born in Chester County, Pa., March 12, 1822, and died in New York, May 11, 1872. He resided in Philadelphia, Cincinnati, New York and Boston. One of his noted paintings, a picture of General Sheridan on his fiery war-horse, was being displayed in a shop-window on Fourth Street, Cincinnati, when one day the artist and James E. Murdoch, elocutionist and actor, were passing by. Murdoch was to give a reading at the opera house that evening, and he exclaimed, "If you will write a poem about that picture, I will read it tonight." Mr. Read went home and a few hours later the following poem was read before a crowded, enthusiastic audience.

Up from the South at break of day,
Bringing to Winchester fresh dismay,
The affrighted air with a shudder bore

Like a herald in haste to the Chieftain's door
The terrible grumble and rumble and roar,
Telling the battle was on once more
And Sheridan twenty miles away.

And wider still those billows of War
Thundered along the horizon's bar;
And louder yet into Winchester rolled
The war of that red sea uncontrolled,
Making the blood of the listener cold
As he thought of the stake in that fiery fray,
And Sheridan twenty miles away.

But there 's a road from Winchester town,
A good broad highway leading down —
And then through the flush of the morning light
A steed as black as the steeds of night
Was seen to pass as was eagle flight.
As if he knew the terrible need,
He stretched away with his utmost speed;
Hills rose and fell, but his heart was gay,
With Sheridan fifteen miles away.

Still sprung from those swift hoofs thundering south
The dust like the smoke from the cannon's mouth,
Or the trail of a comet, sweeping faster and faster,
Foreboding to traitors the doom of disaster.
The heart of the steed and the heart of the master
Were beating like prisoners assaulting their walls,
Impatient to be where the battlefield calls.
Every nerve of the charger was strained to full play
With Sheridan only ten miles away.

Under his spurning feet the road
Like an arrowy alpine river flowed,
And the landscape fell away behind
Like an ocean flying before the wind,
And the steed like a bark fed with furnace ire
Swept on with his wild eyes full of fire.
But lo! he is nearing his heart's desire,
He is snuffing the smoke of the roaring fray,
With Sheridan only five miles away.

The first that the General saw were the groups
Of stragglers; and then the retreating troops!
What was done? What to do? A glance told him both.
Then striking his spurs, with a terrible oath
He dashed down the line mid a storm of huzzas
And the wave of retreat checked its course then because
The sight of the master compelled it to pause.
With foam and with dust the black charger was gray,
By the flash of his eye and his red nostrils' play
He seemed to the whole great army to say,
"I have brought you Sheridan all the way
From Winchester down to save the day.

Hurrah! Hurrah! for Sheridan!
Hurrah! Hurrah! for horse and man!
And when their statues are placed on high
Under the dome of the Union sky,
The American soldiers' Temple of Fame,
There, with the glorious General's name,
Be it said in letters both bold and bright,
"Here is the steed that saved the day
By carrying Sheridan into the fight
From Winchester twenty miles away!"

The following song of the colored troops was printed in the
Missouri *Democrat*, a strong Union paper of St. Louis, in 1863.

SONG OF THE FIRST ARKANSAS REGIMENT

O! we 're the bully soldiers of the First of Arkansaw,
We are fighting for the Union, we are fighting for the law;
We can hit a rebel further than a white man ever saw.
        As we go marching on.

See, there above the centre, where the flag is waving bright,
We are coming out of slavery, we 're bound for freedom's light.
We are going to show Jeff Davis how the African can fight.
        As we go marching on.

We are done with hoeing cotton, we are done with hoeing corn;
We are colored Yankee soldiers now, as sure as you are born;
When the massas hear us yelling they will think it 's Gabriel's Horn
      As we go marching on.

They will have to pay us wages, the wages of their sin;
They will have to bow the forehead to their colored kith and kin;
They will have to give us house-room or the roof shall tumble in;
      As we go marching on.

We have heard the proclamation, massa hush it as he will;
The bird he sing it to us hopping on the cotton hill,
And the 'possum up the gum tree, he could n't keep it still,
      As he went climbing on.

They said, "Now, my colored brethren, you shall be forever free,
From the first of January, eighteen hundred sixty-three."
We hear it in the river going rushing to the sea,
      As it went sounding on.

Father Abraham has spoken, and the message he has sent;
The prison doors he opened, and out the prisoners went,
To join the sable army of the African descent,
      As it goes marching on.

Then fall in, colored brethren, you had better do it soon;
Don't you hear the drum a-beating the "Yankee Doodle" tune?
We are with you now this morning, we 'll be far away at noon,
      As we go marching on.

FAR AWAY THE CAMP FIRES BURN

By Mercadante

Far away the campfires burn —
  We can see their ruddy light
From the distant hill tops flash,
  Bright'ning up the brow of night.

There our brave boys watch and wait,
    While at home both night and day
Mem'ries sweet we treasure up
    Of the absent far away.

Thus while they for freedom fight,
    Our spirits yet shall ever yearn
For that happy day, haste happy day !
    When they shall victorious return.

Onward brothers for the right,
    Blessings on you as you go
Panoplied for freedom's fight,
    Naught but blessing shall we know.

From our altars prayers arise,
    From our homes shall songs ascend ;
He Who ruleth in the skies
    Shall your every step defend.

"We Are Coming, Father Abraham, Three Hundred Thousand More" was written by James Sloan Gibbons, son of the late Dr. Wm. Gibbons, of Wilmington, Del., and a descendant of the Chester County family of that name, who settled in Westtown and Thornbury townships about 1682, part of their land being that now comprised in the Westtown school property.

James Sloan Gibbons moved to New York city, where he became prominent in the anti-slavery movement, being a close friend of Wm. Lloyd Garrison, the Grimke sisters and other leaders of those days. He married Abby Hopper, a daughter of Isaac T. Hopper, the Quaker philanthropist, and their home became a meeting place for all who desired to uplift the distressed.

The poem was written in response to President Lincoln's call, in 1862, for three hundred thousand men. It was written at white heat and published anonymously in the New York *Evening Post*. A full account of its origin and the accompanying circumstances was published some years ago in *Scribner's Magazine*. The poem made an immediate and profound impression, was set to music and was sung all over the country by thousands of men replying to the President's call.

In the draft riots of 1863, when New York was for some days under mob rule, Mr. Gibbons' well-known anti-slavery principles made him a marked man for the hatred of the rioters. A smear of tar upon his front door was the warning of what he might expect. A few hours later the mob surged into his house, which they completely sacked, destroying everything which could not be carried away. Mr. Gibbons himself, learning what was going on, mingled with the crowd, and, unrecognized, witnessed the pillaging and ruin of his cherished home. His wife and eldest daughter were at this time nursing in the army hospitals in the South, but two other daughters had only time to escape by a trap-door across the neighboring roofs to a friendly house around a corner, where they were met by their friend, Joseph H. Choate, who conveyed them to a place of safety.

WE ARE COMING, FATHER ABRAHAM
James S. Gibbons

We are coming, Father Abraham, three hundred thousand more,
From Mississippi's winding stream and from New England's shore;
We leave our ploughs and workshops, our wives and children too.
With hearts too full for utterance, with but a silent tear;
We dare not look behind us, but steadfastly before;
We are coming, Father Abraham, three hundred thousand more!

If you look across the hill-tops that meet the northern sky,
Long moving lines of rising dust your vision may descry;
And now the wind, an instant, tears the cloudy veil aside,
And floats aloft our spangled flag in glory and in pride,
And bayonets in the sunlight gleam, and bands brave music pour;
We are coming, Father Abraham, three hundred thousand more!

If you look all up our valleys where the growing harvests shine
You may see our sturdy farmer boys fast forming into line;
And children from their mother's knees are pulling at the weeds
And learning how to reap and sow against their country's needs;
And a farewell group stands weeping at every cottage door;
We are coming, Father Abraham, three hundred thousand more!

You have called us, and we 're coming, by Richmond's bloody tide,
To lay us down, for Freedom's sake, our brothers' bones beside,
Or from foul treason's savage grasp to wrench the murderous blade,
And in the face of foreign foes its fragments to parade,
Six hundred thousand loyal men and true have gone before;
We are coming, Father Abraham, three hundred thousand more!

TWILIGHT ON SUMTER

RICHARD HENRY STODDARD

Still and dark along the sea
 Sumter lay;
A light was overhead,
As from burning cities shed,
And the clouds were battle-red,
 Far away.
Not a solitary gun
Left to tell the fort had won
 Or lost the day!
Nothing but the tattered rag
Of the drooping rebel flag,
And the sea-birds screaming round it in their play.

How it woke one April morn,
 Fame shall tell;
As from Moultrie, close at hand,
And the batteries on the land,
Round its faint but fearless band
 Shot and shell
Raining hid the doubtful light;
But they fought the hopeless fight
 Long and well
(Theirs the glory, ours the shame!)
Till the walls were wrapt in flame,
Then their flag was proudly struck, and Sumter fell!

Now — oh, look at Sumter now,
 In the gloom!
Mark its scarred and shattered walls,
(Hark! the ruined rampart falls!)
There 's a justice that appalls
 In its doom;

We are coming, Father Abraham, three hundred thousand more,
From Mississippi's winding stream, and from New England's shore;
We leave our ploughs and workshops, our wives and children dear,
With hearts too full for utterance—with but a silent tear;
We dare not look behind us, but steadfastly before,—
We are coming Father Abraham, three hundred thousand more!

If you look all up our valleys where the glowing harvests shine,
You may see our sturdy farmer boys fast forming into line;
And children from their mothers' knees are pulling at the weeds,
And learning how to sow and reap against their country's needs;
And a farewell group stands weeping at every cottage door—
We are coming Father Abraham, three hundred thousand more!

If you look across the hill tops that meet the Northern sky,
Long, moving lines of rising dust your vision may descry;
And now the wind, an instant, tears the cloudy veil aside,
And floats aloft our spangled flag in glory and in pride;
And bayonets in the sunlight gleam, and bands brave music pour—
We are coming Father Abraham, three hundred thousand more!

You have called us, and we 're coming, by Richmond's bloody tide,
To lay us down, for Freedom's sake, our brothers' bones beside;
Or from foul treason's savage grasp to wrench the murderous blade,
And in the face of foreign foes its fragments to parade;
Six hundred thousand loyal men and true, have gone before—
We are coming Father Abraham, three hundred thousand more!

J. Gibbons

REPRODUCTION OF THE ORIGINAL MANUSCRIPT OF
"WE ARE COMING FATHER ABRAHAM"

For this blasted spot of earth
Where rebellion had its birth
   Is its tomb !
And when Sumter sinks at last
From the heavens, that shrink aghast,
Hell shall rise in grim derision and make room !

"Our Color Guard" was written by Captain Thomas J. Diehl
and contributed by his daughter, Mrs. Edward Iungerich Smith,
of 1613 Spruce Street, Philadelphia, a member of the Pennsylvania Society.

Captain Diehl, a Philadelphia lawyer, a captain in the Union
Army and later prominent in social circles, served with high
honor in the Civil War, resigning in 1863 because of the fact that
he never fully recovered from an attack of typhoid fever. In
the first part of the war he was a member of the First Troop,
Philadelphia City Cavalry, and later was commissioned Captain
and made aide to Gen. David B. Birney of the Twenty-third
Pennsylvania Regiment.

"Our Color Guard," which was adopted as a great rallying
song, was written by Captain Diehl in the early days of the war
and it spread like wildfire through the Northern Army.

OUR COLOR GUARD
CAPT. THOMAS J. DIEHL

Now onward ! onward ! let it wave
   Amid the cannon's roar,
Borne by the noble and the brave,
   Through streams of crimson gore ;
Amid the battle's fiercest strife,
   There ever let it be,
And guard it with devoted life,
   That standard of the Free.

CHORUS

Hurrah boys ! Hurrah boys !
Hurrah boys ! Hurrah !
Onward ! onward ever be
"Our Color Guard" supplied.

"Stand by those colors!" many an eye
　　Is looking up today,
To see that glorious emblem fly
　　Where danger checks the way.
"Stand by those colors!" many a soul
　　Will gain new strength to die,
If in the red tides fiercest roll
　　Those colors proudly fly.

On! color guard! Oh noble, brave
　　How one by one they fall,
But not their fate! nor yet the grave
　　Our brave lads can appal.
Now from the ranks leap eagerly,
　　Like groom to meet his bride,
A score of volunteers — and see!
　　"Our color guard" supplied.

Walt Whitman (born 1819 — died 1892), who received little
recognition in his lifetime, has since been acknowledged as one of
the most powerful and original poets America has yet produced.

He was passionately interested in the cause of the North, which
to him was the cause of Freedom — his great ideal. During the
war he devoted his time to caring for the wounded in the Washington hospitals. He was not only a skillful nurse, but had a real
understanding of the common man which made the soldiers watch
him with adoring eyes as he passed through the wards. This work,
with its exposure to contagion and its constant drain on his sym-
pathies, permanently injured his health.

"O Captain! My Captain!" reflects his enthusiasm for the
cause and his great faith in Lincoln.

O CAPTAIN! MY CAPTAIN!

WALT WHITMAN

O Captain! My Captain! our fearful trip is done;
The ship has weathered every rack, the prize we sought is won;
The port is near, the bells I hear, the people all exulting,
While follow eyes the steady keel, the vessel grim and daring;

But O heart! heart! heart!
　　O the bleeding drops of red,
　　　　Where on the deck my Captain lies,
　　　　　　Fallen cold and dead!

O Captain! My Captain! rise up and hear the bells;
Rise up — for you the flag is flung — for you the bugle trills;
For you bouquets and ribbon'd wreaths — for you the shores a-crowding;
For you they call, the swaying mass, their eager faces turning;
　　Here, Captain! dear father!
　　　　This arm beneath your head;
　　　　　　It is some dream that on the deck
　　　　　　　　You 've fallen cold and dead.

My Captain does not answer, his lips are pale and still;
My father does not feel my arms, he has no pulse nor will;
The ship is anchor'd safe and sound, its voyage closed and done;
From fearful trip the victor ship comes in with object won;
　　Exult, O shores, and ring, O bells!
　　　　But I, with mournful tread,
　　　　　　Walk the deck my Captain lies,
　　　　　　　　Fallen, cold and dead.

George Pope Morris, author of "The Flag of Our Union," was a journalist and poet, born in Philadelphia, 1802, died in New York, 1864. He founded the *New York Mirror*, a weekly literary journal, later known as the *New Mirror* and the *Evening Mirror*. Many of the early writings of Bryant, Poe, Hallett and Willis first appeared in its columns. In 1846 Morris established the *Natural Press*, of which the name was changed a year later to the *Home Journal*. In conjunction with N. P. Willis he continued to edit it until later in life.

His best known poems were "Woodman, Spare that Tree," "A Long Time Ago," and "My Mother's Bible."

THE FLAG OF OUR UNION

GEORGE P. MORRIS

[Written 1851]

A song for our banner, the watch-word recall,
    Which gave the Republic her station,
"United we stand, divided we fall;"
    It made and preserved us a nation.

CHORUS

The union of lakes, the union of lands,
    The union of States none can sever!
The union of hearts, the union of hands,
    The flag of our Union forever.

What God in His infinite wisdom designed,
    And armed with the weapons of thunder,
Not all the earth's despots or factions combined,
    Have the power to conquer or sunder.

CHORUS

A SONG OF THE FLAG

M. WOOLSEY STRYKER

Roll a river wide and strong,
    Like the tides a swinging;
Lift the joyful floods of song,
    Set the mountains ringing.

CHORUS

Run the lovely banner high!
    Morning's crimson glory,
Field as blue as God's own sky,
    And every star a story.

Drown the guns, outsound the bells,
    In the rocking steeple,
While the chorus throbs and swells
    Of a happy people.

CHORUS

For our darling flag we sing,
  Pride of all the nation,
Flag that never knew a king,
  Freedom's constellation.

CHORUS

Blest be God, fraternal wars
  Once for all are ended,
And the gashes and the scars
  Peace and time have mended.

CHORUS

Massachusetts, Maryland,
  Tennessee, Nebraska,
One, Columbia's daughters stand
  From Georgia to Alaska.

CHORUS

Staff and masthead swing it forth —
  Liberty unblighted,
West and East and South and North
  Evermore united.

CHORUS

"When Johnny Comes Marching Home Again" was written by Patrick Sarsfield Gilmore, an American musical conductor of Irish birth. He came to Boston in 1847, where, in 1869, he arranged the Peace Jubilee. Later he formed the famous Twenty-Second Regiment Band in New York. He composed the anthem "Columbia" for a national hymn.

WHEN JOHNNY COMES MARCHING HOME
Patrick Sarsfield Gilmore

When Johnny comes marching home again,
  Hurrah! hurrah!
We 'll give him a hearty welcome then,
  Hurrah! hurrah!

The men will cheer, the boys will shout,
The ladies, they will all turn out,
　　And we 'll all feel gay,
When Johnny comes marching home.

The old church bell will peal with joy,
　　Hurrah! hurrah!
To welcome home our darling boy,
　　Hurrah! hurrah!
The village lads and lassies say,
With roses they will strew the way;
　　And we 'll all feel gay,
When Johnny comes marching home

Get ready for the jubilee,
　　Hurrah! hurrah!
We 'll give the hero three times three
　　Hurrah! hurrah!
The laurel-wreath is ready now
To place upon his loyal brow,
　　And we 'll all feel gay,
When Johnny comes marching home.

Let love and friendship on that day,
　　Hurrah! hurrah!
Their choicest treasures then display,
　　Hurrah! hurrah!
And let each one perform some part,
To fill with joy the warrior's heart;
　　And we 'll all feel gay,
When Johnny comes marching home.

WAIT FOR THE WAGON
Or
A Hundred Thousand Northmen

A hundred thousand Northmen
In glittering war array,
Shout "Onward now to Richmond,"
We 'll brook no more delay.

Why give the traitors time and means
To fortify the way
With stolen guns and ambuscades?
Oh, answer us, we pray.

CHORUS

You must wait for the wagons,
The real Army wagons,
The fat contract wagons
Bought in the red-tape way.

Now, if for Army wagons,
Not for compromise you wait,
Just ask them of the farmers,
Of any Union State.
And if you need ten thousand,
Sound, sound the second hand,
You 'll find upon the instant
A supply for your demand.

CHORUS

Wait for the wagons
The new Army wagons,
The fat contract wagons
Till the fifteenth of July.

No growling, fat contractors
Shall block the proper way
Nor real compromisers,
'T is treason's reckoning day.
Then shout again our war-cry:
To Richmond onward move.
We can now rush the traitors,
And that we mean to prove.

CHORUS

You must wait for the wagon
The real Army wagon,
The fat contract wagon
Bought in the red-tape way.

Johanna Mockel, authoress of "The Soldier's Farewell," was born in Bonn, in 1810. Her father was a teacher of literature. She married a publisher named Matthieus, but was divorced from him, and later married Gottfried Kinkel, a professor, poet and advanced democrat. Poor Kinkel was imprisoned for his liberal views, and his wife fled with him to England, where she died in consequence of an accidental fall from a window.

THE SOLDIER'S FAREWELL

JOHANNA MOCKEL

How can I bear to leave thee,
One parting kiss I give thee;
And then whate'er befalls me,
I go where honour calls me.

CHORUS

Farewell, farewell, my own true love,
Farewell, farewell, my own true love.

Ne'er more may I behold thee,
Or to this heart enfold thee,
With spear and pennon glancing,
I see the foe advancing.

CHORUS

I think of thee with longing,
Think thou, when tears are thronging,
What with my last faint sighing,
I 'll whisper soft while dying.

CHORUS

THE BONNIE BLUE FLAG

Composed and sung by Harry Macarthy (the Arkansas comedian) at his personation concerts. Published in New Orleans in 1864, and dedicated to Albert G. Pike, the poet-lawyer of Arkansas.

We are a band of brothers
   And native to the soil,
Fighting for our Liberty,
   With treasure, blood and toil;
And when our rights were threaten'd,
   The cry rose near and far,
Hurrah for the Bonnie Blue Flag
   That bears a Single Star.

CHORUS

   Hurrah! Hurrah! for
   Southern Rights, Hurrah!
   Hurrah for the Bonnie Blue Flag
   That bears a Single Star.

As long as the Union
   Was faithful to her trust,
Like friends and like brethren
   Kind were we and just;
But now when Northern treachery
   Attempts our rights to mar,
We hoist on high the Bonnie Blue Flag
   That bears a Single Star.

CHORUS

First, gallant South Carolina
   Nobly made the stand;
Then came Alabama,
   Who took her by the hand;
Next, quickly, Mississippi,
   Georgia and Florida,
All rais'd on high the Bonnie Blue Flag
   That bears a Single Star.

CHORUS

Ye men of valor, gather round
   The Banner of the Right,
Texas and fair Louisiana,
   Join us in the fight;

Davis, our loved President,
  And Stephens, Statesman rare,
Now rally round the Bonnie Blue Flag
  That bears a Single Star.

CHORUS

And here 's to brave Virginia!
  The Old Dominion State
With the young Confederacy
  At length has link'd her fate;
Impell'd by her example,
  Now other States prepare
To hoist on high the Bonnie Blue Flag
  That bears a Single Star.

CHORUS

Then cheer, boys
  Raise the joyous shout,
For Arkansas and North Carolina
  Now have both gone out;
And let another rousing cheer
  For Tennessee be given
The Single Star of the Bonnie Blue Flag
  Has grown to be Eleven.

CHORUS

Then here 's to our Confederacy,
  Strong we are and brave,
Like patriots of old,
  We 'll fight our heritage to save;
And rather than submit to shame,
  To die we would prefer,
So cheer for the Bonnie Blue Flag
  That bears a Single Star.

CHORUS

The Maryland Society is fortunate in that its late President, Mrs. William Reed, then a very young girl, had unusual opportunities during the Civil War to gather up many of the fiery lays for which the period was remarkable, and while in Richmond, Va., when forty members of the legislature which endorsed the secession of that state were dining at John Patton's, she played the accompaniment for one of the songs which had been written earlier in the day, but which was adapted and sung to the air "Scots Wha Hae Wi' Wallace Bled."

STAND! THE GROUND 'S YOUR OWN

Stand! the ground 's your own, my brave!
Will ye give it up to slaves,
Will ye look for greener graves,
Hope ye mercy still,
What 's the mercy despots feel,
Hear it in that battle peal!
Read it on yon bristling steel!
Ask it — ye who will.

Fear ye foes who kill for hire,
Will ye to your homes retire,
Look behind you! — they 're afire!
And, before you, see
Who have done it! From the vale
On they come! — and will ye quail,
Leaden rain and iron hail
Let their welcome be!

In the God of battles trust!
Die we may, — and die we must;
But, oh where can dust to dust
Be consigned so well,
As where Heaven its dews shall shed
On the martyr'd patriot's bed,
And the rocks shall raise their head
Of his deeds to tell.

"Maryland, My Maryland" was written by James Ryder Randall, an American journalist and poet born in Baltimore, 1859, died in Augusta, Ga., in 1908. He was educated in Georgetown College. Afterwards he was the editor of the *Constitutionalist* of Augusta, and later of the *Morning Star* of New Orleans.

In addition to "Maryland" he wrote "Stonewall Jackson" and "There's Life in the Old Land Yet," but neither equalled in popularity the first, which was only exceeded by "Dixie" in the affections of the South.

Mrs. Reed was also present when "Maryland, My Maryland," set to the tune of the old Harvard College song, "Lauriger Horatius," was sung at the house of Mrs. Winn, on Monument Square, by a group of young people, belles and beaux of Baltimore.

This song was set to music by Mr. H. Rozier Dulany of Baltimore and published the day it was written by Miss Rebecca Lloyd Nicholson, now Mrs. Edw. Shippen, formerly of 209 Monument St., Baltimore, Md., who gave to Messrs. Miller and Beacham the copyright.

MARYLAND! MY MARYLAND!

James Ryder Randall

The despot's heel is on thy shore, ➤
    Maryland! My Maryland!
His torch is at thy temple door,
    Maryland! My Maryland!
Avenge the patriotic gore
That flecked the streets of Baltimore,
And be the battle-queen of yore,
    Maryland! My Maryland!

Hark to thy wand'ring son's appeal,
    Maryland! My Maryland!
My mother State to thee I kneel,
    Maryland! My Maryland!
For life and death, for woe and weal,
Thy peerless chivalry reveal,
And gird thy beauteous limbs with steel,
    Maryland! My Maryland!

Thou wilt not cower in the dust,
  Maryland! My Maryland!
Thy beaming sword shall never rust,
  Maryland! My Maryland!
Remember Carroll's sacred trust;
Remember Howard's warlike thrust, —
And all thy slumberers with the just,
  Maryland! My Maryland!

Come! 't is the red dawn of the day,
  Maryland! My Maryland!
Come! with thy panoplied array
  Maryland! My Maryland!
With Ringgold's spirit for the fray,
With Watson's blood, at Monterey,
With fearless Lowe, and dashing May,
  Maryland! My Maryland!

Come! for thy shield is bright and strong,
  Maryland! My Maryland!
Come! for thy dalliance does thee wrong,
  Maryland! My Maryland!
Come! to thine own heroic throng,
That stalks with Liberty along,
And give a new KEY to thy song,
  Maryland! My Maryland!

Dear Mother! burst the tyrant's chain,
  Maryland! My Maryland!
Virginia should not call in vain,
  Maryland! My Maryland!
She meets her sisters on the plain:
"SIC SEMPER," 't is the proud refrain,
That baffles minions back amain,
  Maryland! Maryland!
Arise, in majesty again,
  Maryland! My Maryland!

I see the blush upon thy cheek,
  Maryland! My Maryland!
But thou wast ever bravely meek,
  Maryland! My Maryland!

But lo! there surges forth a shriek
From hill to hill, from creek to creek —
Potomac calls to Chesapeake,
    Maryland! My Maryland!

Thou wilt not yield the vandal toll,
    Maryland! My Maryland!
Thou wilt not crook to his control,
    Maryland! My Maryland!
Better the fire upon thee roll,
Better the blade, the shot, the bowl,
Than crucifixion of the soul,
    Maryland! My Maryland!

I hear the distant thunder hum,
    Maryland! My Maryland!
The Old Line's bugle, fife and drum,
    Maryland! My Maryland!
She is not dead, nor deaf, nor dumb:
Huzza! she spurns the Northern scum!
She breathes — she burns! she 'll come! she 'll come!
    Maryland! My Maryland!

GOD SAVE THE SOUTH

Earnest Halphin   Music by C. M. A. Ellerbrock
Published by Miller and Beacham
The first song published in the South during the war

God save the South!
God save the South!
Her altars and firesides,
God save the South.
Now that the war is nigh,
Chanting our battle-cry
Freedom or death.

CHORUS

Now that the war is nigh,
Now that we aim to die
Chanting the battle-cry
Freedom or death.

What tho' they 're three to one,
Forward each sire and son,
Strike to the grave.

CHORUS

God made the right
Stronger than might;
Millions would trample us,
Down in their pride;
Lay Thou their legions low,
Roll back the ruthless foe,
Let the proud spoiler know,
God on our side!

CHORUS

Mark Honor's call,
Summoning all,
Summoning all of us
Unto the strife.
Sons of the South, awake!
Strike till the brand shall break,
Strike for Honor's sake,
Freedom and life.

CHORUS

Rebels before,
Our fathers of yore,
Rebel 's the righteous name
Washington bore:
Why, then be ours the same,
The name that he snatched from shame,
Making it first in fame
Foremost in war.

CHORUS

War to the hilt,
Theirs be the guilt,
Who fetter the freeman
To ransom the slave.

God be our shield,.
God be our shield,
Stretch thine arm over us,
Strengthen and save.
Up then and undismayed,
Sheath not the battle blade,
Till the last foe is laid
Low in the grave.

CHORUS

God save the South,
God save the South,
Dry the dim eyes that now
Follow our path.
Still let the light feet rove,
Safe through the orange grove,
Still keep the hand we love,
Safe from Thy wrath.

CHORUS

God save the South,
God save the South.
Her altars and friends,
God save the South.
For the great war is nigh,
And we will win or die
Chanting our battle-cry
Freedom or death.

CHORUS

The words of "My Old Kentucky Home" were written by
Stephen Collins Foster, while he was visiting the family of Judge
Rowan at their hospitable and beautiful home, at Bardstown, Ky.
Stephen Collins Foster was born at Pittsburg, Pa., July 4, 1826,
and died in New York, January 13, 1864. He also wrote "Old
Folks at Home" and other popular songs.

MY OLD KENTUCKY HOME

STEPHEN COLLINS FOSTER

The sun shines bright in the old Kentucky home,
    'T is summer, the darkies are gay;
The corn top 's ripe and the meadow 's in the bloom,
    While the birds make music all the day.
The young folks roll on the little cabin floor,
    All merry, all happy and bright;
By'm by hard times come a-knocking at the door,
    Then my old Kentucky home, good night.

CHORUS

Weep no more, my lady,
O weep no more today!
We will sing one song
For the old Kentucky home,
For the old Kentucky home,
Far away.

They hunt no more for the possum and the coon,
    On the meadow, the hill, and the shore;
They sing no more by the glimmer of the moon,
    On the bench by the old cabin door.
The day goes by like a shadow o'er the heart,
    With sorrow where all was delight;
The time has come when the darkies have to part,
    Then my old Kentucky home, good night.

CHORUS

The head must bow and the back will have to bend,
    Wherever the darkey may go;
A few more days, and the trouble all will end,
    In the field where the sugar canes grow.
A few more days for to tote the weary load,
    No matter 't will never be light;
A few more days till we totter on the road,
    Then my old Kentucky home, good night.

CHORUS

SOUTHERN SONG

Written by Maria Grason, of Anne Arundel County, Md., in 1867

Come all ye sons of freedom,
And join the Southern band,
We are going to fight the Yankees,
And drive them from our land.
Justice is our motto,
  And Providence our guide.
So jump into the wagon
  And we 'll all take a ride.

CHORUS

So wait for the wagon
Dissolution wagon,
The South is the wagon, and we 'll
All take a ride.

Secession is our watchword;
  Our rights we all demand
To defend our homes and firesides,
  To pledge our hearts and hands.
Jeff Davis is our President,
  With Stephens by his side,
Great Beauregard, our general,
  He joins us in our ride.

CHORUS

Our wagon is the very best;
  The running gear is good;
Stuffed round the sides with cotton,
  And made of Southern wood.
Carolina is the driver,
  With Georgia by her side;
Virginia holds the flag up
  While we all take a ride.

CHORUS

Old Lincoln and his congressmen
  With Seward by his side,

Put old Scott into the wagon,
    Just for to take a ride,
McDowell was the driver,
    To cross Bull-Run he tried,
But there he left the wagon
    For Beauregard to ride.

CHORUS

The invading tribes called Yankees,
    With Lincoln for their guide,
Tried to keep good old Kentucky,
    From joining in their ride,
But she heeded not their entreaties,
    She has come into the ring,
She would n't fight for Government
    Where cotton was not king.

CHORUS

Manassas was the battle-ground,
    The field was fair and wide,
The Yankees thought they 'd wipe us out
    And on to Richmond ride;
But when they met our ."Dixie" boys,
    Their danger they espied;
They wheeled about for Washington
    And did n't wait to ride.

CHORUS

Brave Beauregard, God bless him !
    Led legions in his stead,
While Johnston seized the colors,
    And waved them o'er his head.
So rising generations,
    With pleasure we will tell,
How bravely our Fisher,
    And gallant Johnston fell.

CHORUS

I'M A GOOD OLD REBEL

Author unknown. Music written by R. BISHOP BUCKLEY, promoter of Buckley's Minstrels, in 1843. He was born in England in 1810, and died in Quincy, Mass., in 1867.

Entered according to Act of Congress 1864 by A. C. Blackmar in the Clerk's office of the U. S. D. Court of Louisiana.

O, I'm a good old rebel,
　　Now that's just what I am,
For this "Fair Land of Freedom,"
　　I do not care a damn;
I'm glad I fit against it,
　　I only wish we'd won,
And I don't want no pardon,
　　For anything I done.

I hates the Constitution,
　　The great republic too;
I hates the Freedman's Buro,
　　In uniform of blue;
I hates the nasty Eagle
　　With all its brass and fuss,
The lyin', thieving Yankees,
　　I hates 'em wuss and wuss.

I hates the Yankee nation,
　　And everything they do,
I hates the Declaration
　　Of Independence too;
I hates the glorious Union,
　　'T is dripping with our blood;
I hates their striped banner,
　　I fit it all I could.

Three hundred thousand Yankees
　　Is stiff in Southern dust;
We got three hundred thousand,
　　Before they conquered us.
They died of Southern fever,
　　And Southern steel and shot,
I wish they was three million,
　　Instead of what we got.

I followed old Mas' Robert,
For four year near about,
Got wounded in three places,
And starved at Point Lookout.
I cotched the roomatism,
A-camping in the snow,
But I killed a chance o' Yankee
I 'd like to kill some mo'.

I can't take up my musket
And fight 'em now no more,
But I ain't a-going to love 'em
Now that is sartin sure;
And I don't want no pardon
For what I was and am,
I won't be reconstructed,
And I don't care a damn.

THE CAVALIER'S GLEE

By Captain Blackford, of General Stuart's Staff   Air: *The Pirate's Glee*

Spur on, Spur on, we love the bounding
Of barbs that bear us to the fray;
"The Charge" our bugles now are sounding,
And our bold Stuart leads the way.

CHORUS

The path of honor lies before us,
Our hated foeman gathers fast,
At home bright eyes are sparkling for us,
And we'll defend them to the last.

Spur on, Spur on, we love the rushing
Of steeds that spurn the turf they tread;
We 'll through the Northern ranks go crushing,
With our proud battle-flag o'erhead.

CHORUS

Spur on, Spur on, we love the flashing
   Of blades that battle to be free;
'T is for our sunny South they 're clashing,
   For household gods and liberty.

CHORUS

STONEWALL JACKSON'S WAY

JOHN WILLIAMSON PALMER
Pub. by Miller and Beacham

The author of this poem was born in Baltimore, Md., April 4, 1825. Early in life he practised medicine in San Francisco; later he resided in New York city, devoting himself, after 1870, to general literature. "Stonewall Jackson's Way" was written at Oakland, Md., on the seventeenth of September, 1862, while the battle of Antietam was in progress. Doctor Palmer died in 1896.

Come, stack arms, men! pile on the rails,
   Stir up the camp-fire bright;
No growling if the canteen fails,
   We 'll make a roaring night.
Here Shenandoah brawls along,
There burly Blue Ridge echoes strong,
To swell the Brigade's rousing song
   Of "Stonewall Jackson's way."

We see him now — the queer slouched hat
   Cocked o'er his eye askew;
The shrewd, dry smile; the speech so pat,
   So calm, so blunt, so true,
The "Blue Light Elder" knows 'em well;
Says he "That 's Banks — he 's fond of shell;
Lord save his soul! we 'll give him — " well!
   That 's "Stonewall Jackson's way."

Silence! ground arms! kneel all! caps off!
   Old Massa 's goin' to pray.
Strangle the fool that dares to scoff!
   Attention! it 's his way.

Appealing from his native sod,
   In forma pauperis to God :
"Lay bare Thine arm ; stretch forth Thy rod !"
   Amen ! That 's "Stonewall Jackson's way."

He 's in the saddle now. Fall in !
   Steady ! the whole brigade !
Hill 's at the ford, cut off ; we 'll win
   His way out, ball and blade !
What matter if our shoes are worn ?
What matter if our feet are torn ?
"Quick step, we 're with him before morn !"
   That 's "Stonewall Jackson's way."

The sun's bright lances rout the mists
   Of morning, and, by George !
Here 's Longstreet, struggling in the lists,
   Hemmed in any ugly gorge.
Pope and his Dutchman whipped before ;
"Bay'nets and grape !" hear Stonewall roar ;
"Charge Stuart ! Pay off Ashby's score !"
   In "Stonewall Jackson's way."

Ah ! Maiden, wait and watch and yearn
   For news of Stonewall's band !
Ah ! Widow, read with eyes that burn,
   That ring upon thy hand.
Ah ! Wife, sew on, pray on, hope on ;
Thy life shall not be all forlorn ;
The foe had better ne'er been born
   That gets in "Stonewall's way."

THE CONQUERED BANNER

FATHER RYAN

Words by MOINA (Rev. Abram J. Ryan). Music by THEOD. VON LAHACHE,
a Roman Catholic Priest of Knoxville, Tenn.)

The words of this song were published first in the *Freeman's Bureau*, June 24, 1865, and later appeared in "Southern Poems of the War," collected and arranged by Miss Emily V. Nason, second edition of which was published in 1868 by John Murphy & Co. of Baltimore.

Furl that Banner! for 't is weary,
Round its staff 't is drooping dreary,
  Furl it, fold it, it is best,
For there 's not a man to wave it,
And there 's not a sword to save it,
In the blood that heroes gave it,
And its foes now scorn and brave it;
  Furl it, hide it, let it rest.

Take that Banner down, 't is tattered,
Broken in its staff and shattered,
And the valiant hosts are scattered
  Over whom it floated high;
Oh! 't is hard for us to fold it
Hard to think there 's none to hold it,
Hard that those who once unrolled it
  Now must furl it with a sigh.

Furl that Banner! furl it sadly;
Once ten thousands hailed it gladly,
And ten thousands wildly, madly,
  Swore it would forever wave,
Swore the foeman's sword could never
Hearts like theirs entwined, dissever
'Till that flag should float forever
  O'er their freedom or their grave.

Furl it, for the hands that grasped it,
And the hearts that fondly clasped it,
  Cold and dead are lying low,
And that Banner, it is trailing,
While around it sounds the wailing
  Of its people in their woe;
For, though conquered, they adore it,
Love the cold, dead hands that bore it,
Weep for those who fell before it,
Pardon those who trailed and tore it,
And oh! wildly they deplore it
  Now to furl and fold it so.

Furl that Banner! true, 't is gory,
Yet 't is wreathed around with glory,
And 't will live in song and story
    Though its folds are in the dust;
For its fame on brightest pages
Penned by poets and by sages,
Shall go sounding down through ages,
    Furl its folds, though now we must.
Furl that Banner softly, slowly,
Treat it gently, it is holy,
For it droops above the dead.
Touch it not, unfold it never,
Let it droop there, furl'd forever!

Daniel Decatur Emmet was a celebrated writer and negro minstrel, born in Ohio in 1815. After serving in the army he joined a circus in 1835, and in 1842 formed the first negro minstrel company, which records appearances in New York, Boston and in England. It was for this company that, in 1859, he wrote "Dixie," which promptly and permanently became the favorite song of the South — though he was himself a Northerner — and among many other songs composed "The Road to Richmond," "Old Dan Tucker," "Walk Along John," and "Early in the Morning."

The accepted theory of the name "Dixie Land" is that it was suggested from Mason's and Dixon's Line, which was originally a line of survey between Pennsylvania on the north and Maryland on the south. The first words used for the song in the South were from a poem published in Charleston in 1861. Gen. Albert Pike, a Boston man, has written other words of some literary merit. He had served with distinction in the Mexican War, and on the breaking out of the war between the United States he enlisted on the Confederate side with a force of Cherokee Indians, whom he led at the battle of Pea Ridge.

DIXIE'S LAND
DANIEL DECATUR EMMET

I wish I was in de land ob cotton,
Old times dar am not forgotten,
    Look away! look away! look away! Dixie land.

In Dixie land, whar I was born in,
Early on one frosty mornin',
    Look away ! look away ! look away ! Dixie land.

CHORUS

Den I wish I was in Dixie,
Horray ! Horray !
In Dixie land I 'll take my stand,
To lib and die in Dixie !
Away, away, away down South in Dixie !
Away, away, away down South in Dixie !

Old Missus marry Will de weaber,
William was a gay deceaber,
    Look away ! look away ! look away ! Dixie land.
But when he put his arm around 'er
He smiled as fierce as a forty-pounder,
    Look away ! look away ! look away ! Dixie land.

His face was sharp as a butcher's cleaber,
But dat did not seem to greab 'er
    Look away ! look away ! look away ! Dixie land.
Old Missus acted the foolish part,
And died for a man dat broke her heart,
    Look away ! look away ! look away ! Dixie land.

Now here 's a health to the next old Missus,
And all de gals dat want to kiss us,
    Look away ! look away ! look away ! Dixie land.
But if you want to drive 'way sorrow,
Come and hear dis song tomorrow,
    Look away ! look away ! look away ! Dixie land.

Dar 's buckwheat cakes an' Ingen batter,
Makes you fat, or a little fatter,
    Look away ! look away ! look away ! Dixie land.
Den hoe it down an' scratch your grabble.
To Dixie's land I 'm bound to trabble,
    Look away ! look away ! look away ! Dixie land.

THE SPANISH–AMERICAN WAR

CHAPTER V

THE SPANISH–AMERICAN WAR

THE SPANISH-AMERICAN WAR was a small war with great and unsuspected consequences for the United States. It found us a busy, self-centred nation of about seventy-six millions population, minding our own business and giving little thought to world affairs. It left us, as we have been left by the Great War, with our dreams of national isolation rudely shattered.

It was eighty-four years since we had had a foreign war. The breach caused by the Civil War had become healed and we were profoundly at peace with the world. Our utter lack of military preparedness cannot be more strikingly expressed than by the fact that for every thousand inhabitants there was less than one-quarter of a regular army soldier; or, in other words, a ratio of one soldier to 2700 people.

Fortunately our Navy, small as it was, had been kept in good training, for the war, to a possibly greater extent than that of 1812, was to be decided on the seas.

The Cuban Revolution of 1895 had been easily quelled by Spain, which, under the leadership of General Weyler, followed up its armed invasion with a most cruel policy of suppression through starvation.

President Cleveland in 1896 gave a gentle warning to the "Dons" in his annual message stating, "It cannot be reasonably assumed that the hitherto expectant attitude of the United States will be indefinitely maintained."

McKinley continued the policy of "Watchful Waiting" (which was no new thing in our military history) until the dramatic and tragic destruction of the battleship *Maine* at Havana on February 15, 1898, aroused the country to a fighting pitch. On April eleventh President McKinley in a message to Congress declared "In the name of humanity, in the name of civilization, in behalf of endangered American interests — the war in Cuba must stop," and on the anniversary of the battle of Lexington, as well as that of the first blood shed in our Civil War, Congress resolved that

Cuba "must be free." War was formally declared on April 25, 1898.

Exciting events followed in rapid succession. On the first day of May Dewey destroyed the Spanish squadron. The battleship *Oregon* made her famous fourteen thousand mile voyage from San Francisco to Cuba and reported ready for action. Lieutenant Hobson, with unsurpassed daring, sank the collier *Merrimac* in an unsuccessful attempt to bottle up the Spanish fleet in the harbor of Santiago de Cuba. San Juan was captured on July 2 after a brilliant assault led by Colonel Roosevelt and his "Rough Riders."

On the following day Admiral Cervera's attempt to escape with his fleet from Santiago was frustrated by the squadron under Admirals Sampson and Schley, which destroyed the entire Spanish fleet.

Gen. Nelson A. Miles invaded Porto Rico late in July and his easy progress was arrested only by the peace protocol of August thirteenth after a war of three months.

The regular army had in this time been increased by Congressional act to 61,000 and 216,000 men had volunteered for service.

In this brief, decisive war all the elements seem to have existed for the creation of an inspired succession of war songs.

The writers were prolific, but the results are a greater evidence of the ambition of our publishers than the genius of our authors and composers.

A book of Spanish-American War Songs collected by Sidney A. Witherbee contains some nine hundred pages of verse.

It is not invidious to remark, since practically none of the songs have been in popular use, that the inspiration of the war that liberated Cuba and alleviated the Philippines was barren of marked results so far as heroic verse production is concerned. One song of this era which gained but little notoriety in its day, was deservedly revived during the World War. We refer to "America the Beautiful" by Katharine Lee Bates and sung to a beautiful old hymn tune, Materna.

It is difficult to account for the mediocrity of the war songs of this period, except for the fact that American poetry and musical composition were both then in a generally innocuous condition.

The significance of the events is greater in perspective than they seemed at the moment. Perhaps our writers, as well as our fighters, were caught unprepared.

The chief sources of inspiration for the Spanish War Songs seem to have been Dewey at Manila Bay, "Remember the Maine," "Cuba Libre," on each of which subjects there are numerous poems. Roosevelt's Rough Riders were also popular; Captain Hobson, and "The Man behind the Gun," and there were many verses written to the tunes of songs used in the earlier wars. But of war songs which were popular among the soldiers and sailors there are few which have survived. Perhaps the most stirring is John Philip Sousa's "The Stars and Stripes Forever. which was written shortly before the war, but not for the war,"

Although the mystery of the sinking of the *Maine* has never been satisfactorily solved, the event caused much excitement throughout the United States, and gave rise to more poetry than any other event of the war. Hence the many effusions on "Remember the Maine," with which phrase in their minds the American forces entered the war.

One of the most pleasing subjects, as well as popular, was the final reconciliation of North and South — united once again in their common cause.

AMERICA THE BEAUTIFUL

KATHARINE LEE BATES, Professor of English, Wellesley College   Air: *Materna*
Permission to reprint in this volume graciously given by the author

> O beautiful for spacious skies,
>   For amber waves of grain,
> For purple mountain majesties
>   Above the fruited plain!
>   America! America!
>   God shed His grace on thee
> And crown thy good with brotherhood
>   From sea to shining sea!
>
> O beautiful for pilgrim feet,
>   Whose stern, impassioned stress
> A thoroughfare for freedom beat

Across the wilderness!
America! America!
God mend thine every flaw,
Confirm thy soul in self-control,
Thy liberty in law!

O beautiful for heroes proved
In liberating strife,
Who more than self their country loved,
And mercy more than life!
America! America!
May God thy gold refine
Till all success be nobleness
And every gain divine!

O beautiful for patriot dream
That sees beyond the years
Thine alabaster cities gleam
Undimmed by human tears!
America! America!
God shed His grace on thee
And crown thy good with brotherhood
From sea to shining sea!

RALLY ROUND THE STANDARD, BOYS
FANNY J. CROSBY

Mrs. Frances Jane Van Alstyne, writer of many popular hymns, died February 12, 1915. This was written to the old tune of "The Battle Cry of Freedom" (new wine in old bottles).

Rally round the standard, boys,
The gallant blue and gray,
Onward where the trumpet voice
Of freedom calls, away!
Death to all oppression,
Is our battle cry today;
On to the rescue of Cuba.

CHORUS

Hurrah! Hurrah! Hurrah for victory;
Hurrah! Hurrah! O glorious jubilee;
When the starry banner of the loyal, brave and free,
Waves o'er the Island of Cuba.

God will give us courage, boys,
Our noble cause to gain;
Trusting Him we 'll overthrow
The tyrant power of Spain;
Soon a shout will echo through
Our country's wide domain,
Telling of freedom for Cuba.

Hail our naval heroes that
Have won a conqueror's name;
Heroes of Manila, by
Our nation crowned with fame,
Imitate their valor and
Their fearless deeds proclaim,
While we are fighting for Cuba.

STANDARD OF A NATION'S PRIDE

Virginia G. Ellard   Air: *Watch on the Rhine*

The Patriot's voice, in glad refrain,
Repeats in loud, triumphant strain,
Our Flag, our Flag, our Banner free,
Float o'er this Land of Liberty.

CHORUS

Oh! Standard of a Nation's pride,
With truth and honor close allied,
Under thy stars and stripes we 'll be,
Bound heart and soul to God and thee.

We 'll greet, as favored sons of earth,
The Flag that hailed our Nation's birth;
This legacy our fathers bought,
This emblem with their suff'ring fraught.

CHORUS

With fervent hearts, at duty's hest,
We 'll guard the land that God has blessed;
While this shall be our clarion cry,
For Freedom's Flag, we 'll dare to die.

CHORUS

Permission to reprint in this volume was courteously granted by the Cincinnati Chapter of the Daughters of the American Revolution.

THE BATTLE SONG OF THE "IOWA"

CLAY M. GREENE   Sung to the Melody: *Marching through Georgia*
[1898]
Permission to reprint in this volume courteously given by the author

Clear the decks for action boys, we 're brave and strong and true,
Rouse again the loyal fire that burned in '62,
Strike a blow for vengeance and our murdered boys in blue,
While we are fighting for Cuba.

REFRAIN

Hurrah, Hurrah! Three times and once again,
Hurrah! Hurrah! The boasted power of Spain
Shall crumble 'neath the battle cry, "Do not forget the *Maine!*"
While we are fighting for Cuba.

Hail to staunch Iowa boys, and hail to fighting Bob,
All our guns are ready, and our engines beat and throb,
Waiting for an order to destroy that Spanish mob,
While we are fighting for Cuba.

Take your lanyards in your hands, the Spaniard is in sight,
Like our gallant Captain we are spoiling for a fight,
For our cause is mighty, and we know that we are right,
While we are fighting for Cuba.

Speed afar across the deep with loud and lusty yell;
Promise what our Captain did, as we have heard 'em tell,
Spanish in a month will be the "parley-voo" of hell,
While we are fighting for Cuba.

THE FREEDOM OF CUBA

ELLA STRAIT HOLLISTER   Air: *Marching through Georgia*

See the cruel bondage of the Spaniard's mighty host,
Placed upon our neighbors, who are dying near our coast;
We must go to free them, and with arms maintain, at most,
  Rights of the people of Cuba.

CHORUS

We bring, we bring the greetings of the free,
We bring, we bring the year of jubilee;
So the chorus rings from friendly hearts across the sea,
Chanting the freedom of Cuba.

Listen to the echoes of a struggling people's groans,
See their haggard faces, hearken to their tearful moans,
Sing out, then, Americans, in no uncertain tones,
    Rights of the people of Cuba.

North and South will send a band of soldiers brave and true,
Fighting under one old flag, the Red, White and Blue;
Flag of hope, a beacon be! and thus flash forth anew,
    Rights of the people of Cuba.

Permission to reprint this song was kindly given by Ella Strait Hollister, member of the Cincinnati Chapter of the Daughters of the American Revolution.

ONWARD FOR CUBA

J. St. George Joyce   Air: *Hail to the Chief*

Sons of Columbia, the war blast is sounding.
    To arms! Your country's aroused for the fray;
O'er valley and hillside the tocsin's resounding,
    And freedom stands forth in grim battle array.
        Then shoulder to shoulder, men,
        Fight the old fight again —
The old fight we've oft waged in Liberty's name.
        Hurl the tyrant low,
        God will approve the blow;
Onward for Cuba, for freedom and fame!

The fair isle of Cuba lies prostrate and dying,
    And famine sweeps o'er the sore stricken land,
From the hill tops the single-star banner is flying,
    While Gomez keeps guard with his patriot band.
        Hark to a people's plaint,
        Hark to their moanings faint,
Hark to that deep wail of anguish and shame!
        Make the base Spaniard feel
        The power of your guns and steel,
Onward for Cuba, for freedom and fame!

Too long has the despot the fair island plundered
    Too long have the people groaned under his sway;
The shackles with which they are bound must be sundered,
    And the slave stand a freeman in the light of God's day!
        Onward! there lies the foe,
        Strike the death-dealing blow.

Your war cry resounding, "Remember the *Maine!*"
  Think of our sailors brave
  Who now lie beneath the wave.
Onward for Cuba! Now vengeance on Spain!

  On for Columbia there,
  Fight the old fight again,
Sons of our Sireland, brave, trusted and true.
  Old Glory flash in the light
  Crimson your steel now bright,
Strike hard for Cuba and the Red, White and Blue!

REMEMBER THE "MAINE"

One version of this song was written by Hamilton Ormsbee.
Music by Dr. G. E. Conterno and was very popular during the
Spanish-American War. There are also many other versions
under this title.

1898 and 1562

SAM WALTER FOSS

The evening and the morning have joined in fight at last,
  Around the Western Islands the old shall fight the new,
Columbia and Hispania, the present and the past,
  And Eighteen Hundred Ninety-eight fights Fifteen Sixty-two!

The nation of the Forward Look that sees the heights ahead,
  Fights with the Backward Glancing Realm that sees the tombs behind
And who shall doubt the conflict of the Quick and of the Dead,
  Of the leaders with the Laggards of Mankind?

Today joins fight with yesterday; the Mediæval years,
  Are grappling with the Modern, and the Old assails the New,
But who, who fears the issue? where's the trembling soul that fears,
  When Eighteen Hundred Ninety-eight fights Fifteen Sixty-two.

THE STARS AND STRIPES FOREVER

John Philip Sousa

The accompanying letter from Mr. Sousa was procured for this volume by the District of Columbia Society.

"I was in Europe in the Fall of 1896 and was called suddenly back to America. I was extremely lonely and anxious to return. I sailed from Liverpool on the White Star Line *The Teutonic*, and during the voyage the melodies of 'The Stars and Stripes Forever' came to me, as I paced the deck with a mental brass band playing the march fully a hundred times during the week I was on the steamer." The manuscript of the march when completed is dated December 25, 1896. It was first publicly performed in Philadelphia some time during the season of 1897.

Let martial note in triumph float,
    And liberty extend its mighty hand,
A flag appears 'mid thund'rous cheers,
    The banner of the Western land.
        The emblem of the brave and true,
        Its folds protect no tyrant crew,
        The red and white and starry blue,
        In Freedom's shield and hope.
Other nations may deem their flags the best,
    And cheer them with fervid elation,
But the flag of the North and South and West
    Is the flag of flags — the flag of Freedom's nation.

CHORUS

Hurrah for the flag of the free!
May it wave as our standard forever!
The gem of the land and the sea,
The banner of the Right.
Let despots remember the day
When our fathers with mighty endeavor,
Proclaimed as they march'd to the fray,
That by their might, and by their right,
    It waves forever!

Let eagle shriek from lofty peak,
  The never ending watch-word of our land —
Let summer breeze waft through the trees
  The echo of the chorus grand.
    Sing out for Liberty and right!
    Sing out for Freedom and light!
    Sing out for Union and its might!
    Oh, patriotic sons!
Other nations may deem their flags the best
  And cheer them with fervid elation,
But the flag of the North and South and West
  Is the flag of flags, the flag of Freedom's nation.

Used by permission of The John Church Co., owners of the copyright.

THERE'LL BE A HOT TIME IN THE OLD TOWN TONIGHT

Another prominent song of the Spanish American War was "There 'll Be a Hot Time in the Old Town Tonight". This song was written by Theodore Metz and published in 1897 and during the Spanish American War it was adopted by the soldiers as a marching song and became immensely popular.

"On the Banks of the Wabash" was another very popular song of this period.

WORLD WAR

CHAPTER VI

WORLD WAR

THERE are a few simple facts which may well be borne in mind as we approach our War Songs of the last great conflict. The area of the main portion of the United States in 1917 was 3,026,-789 square miles. Alaska and our insular possessions add 716,729 square miles, making a total of 3,743,518 square miles. We had in continental United States, exclusive of Alaska, an average of 36 persons per square mile. England has an average population of 624 per square mile, and if all the people in the world were transported to continental United States our average density of population would still be less than that of England.

It was not only our man power that the Allies hoped to enlist in the war, but our vast economic resources, for the United States had become the greatest producer of food and manufacturing material in the world.

Not only had our population increased in complexity, but it had changed greatly in its living habits. Whereas in 1800 only about four per cent resided in cities, in 1890, 28 per cent, and in 1910, 46 per cent — at the time of the World War about 50 per cent of our citizens were urban.

The relative strength of the army to the population in 1910 was 8/100 of one per cent, which happens also to have been the same in the year 1800. By 1918 this strength of the army had risen to the unprecedented figure of three and one-half per cent.

The problem that faced the Nation when war was finally declared was not only to expand the fighting forces from 190,000 in March, 1917, to 3,665,000 in November, 1918, but to prepare the minds of an unhomogeneous public for war, and to arouse the people to give their unstinted financial support to the government.

For the first time in American history the power of song was deliberately enlisted in "putting over" this herculean task.

In the military camps song leaders were appointed and the men were encouraged to sing stirring and patriotic songs. Re-

cruiting was stimulated by the employment of professional sing-
ers in great open air concerts. The salesmen for Liberty Bonds
were "gingered up" at their daily sales meetings during the
drives by song singing under skilled leadership.

Music was even carried well up to the trenches by organizations
which performed in the rest camps and hospitals to bring cheer
and good spirits to the soldiers. Community singing during this
conflict came into its own, and happily seems destined to survive.

Lt. Gitz Rice, a soldier who knew his men and what they liked
wrote many songs that were most popular. He above all others
wrote that which interpreted the thoughts and emotions of his
men. It is to be regretted that we are unable to get the words
of his many songs, which is due to complications on copyrights.
"Dear Old Pal of Mine" was perhaps his most famous song.

The events of the war are too fresh to need any review, and
our chief interest in this chapter is to record the songs which
were used for the purposes just outlined.

As in previous wars, some of the songs were marked by high
patriotic sentiments, some appealed to the fighting spirit, and
others to the sentimental aspects of the situation. There is distinctly more humor in the songs that became popular than in
those of any previous war era. Our boys went smiling and singing
into this war.

In spite of our dependence on the Navy for transportation and
defense, only one song appears to have been written with the
sailors in mind. Doubtless because we participated in no great
naval battles and also owing to the secrecy with which submarine
encounters were guarded by the Navy Department, dramatic
incidents, such as characterized the War of 1812 and are reflected
in its songs, were lacking, either to inspire composition or to
stir the public enthusiasm.

Thus the courageous, effective work of our Navy came in for
singularly little popular notice or praise. Partly for this reason
and partly on account of the literary merit of the composition
itself, we start this collection with "The Song of Then and Now,"
which has the real tang of the ocean.

THE SONG OF THEN AND NOW
JAMES BARNES

Oh, they sang a song of Wind and Sail
  In the days of heave and haul,
Of the weather-gage, of tack and sheet,
When the anchor rose to the tramp of feet
  And the click of capstan pawl.
They sang brave songs of the old broadsides,
  Long Tom, and the cannonade!
Hi! cutlass and pike, as the great sides strike—
  Ho! the cheers of the ne'er-afraid!
For they cheered as they fought, did those sailor-men;
  They stripped to the buff for the fray —
It was steel to steel, it was eye to eye,
  They stripped to the buff for the fray —
It was steel to steel, it was eye to eye,
Yard-arm to yard-arm against the sky!
  All ye boarders, up and away!

They sang of the men of the quarterdeck,
  Brave deeds of those captains bold!
Never a name but was known to fame,
  And was hailed in the days of old.
Let us sing the song of the fighting men,
  The life of the plunging bow —
The good old song of the Sea and the Ship,
  The song of the Then and Now!

Gone are the days of the heave and haul
  (Think ye our blood has thinned?)
We're slaves of steam and science,
  Not laborers of the wind!
Oh, the cable comes in to the cable tiers,
  And no one lifts a hand;
The clank of a bell sounds out, "That's well!"
  And the engines understand!
We come in 'gainst the wind and the tide at night,
  And go out 'gainst the storm in the morn.
(But think ye our arms have lost their might?
  Think ye our locks are shorn?)

Past are the days of Wind and Sail,
   We've cast off the thrall of the sea,
We take no heed of the weather-gage —
   No fear of the rocks on the lee.
We come and we go in the fiercest blow
    (It is food for our roaring fires!)
For the great screws churn, and the huge hulls turn
   As the Soul of each Ship desires!
The spirit, the strength, and the will are there,
   The sea has not changed her men;
The Vessel must do, and the men must dare,
   And Now is the same as Then!

They raked and they fought at pistol-shot,
   We fight at ten miles and more.
(Think ye their dangers discount ours,
   Ye men of books ashore?)
The turret turns and the guns are trained —
   But not in the older way;
The conning-tower is the place of power
   And the Soul of the Ship holds away.
But in sponson, turret, and close barbette,
   Or below in the noxious air,
Are brave forms covered with blood and sweat —
   The fighting men are there!

There are dangers our fathers wot not of
   (In the days of wind and sail)
The unseen foes and the sighted Death,
   With the foam along the rail.
The channels are filled with uncouth shapes
   That lurk below in the brine —
The force of fifty ships is there
   In the sullen, sunken mine!
Tho' no orders come from the quarter-deck,
   Hear the rip of the rapid fire!
Full speed ahead, astern, or check,
   At a spark from the listening wire!

And the ship she trembles from top to keel —
Thro' her forty thousand tons!
And her scorched decks leap with a thundering throb
   'Neath the roar of her mighty guns!
Dented, and tortured, and pierced, she stands
   The blows on her ringing plates;
Grimy and blank she signals back
   To the flags of her fighting mates.
Hear the grinding crash from her armored prow,
   Hear the rattling fire from the mast?
Young "Steel Flanks," of the living Now
   Is "Old Ironsides" of the past!

Oh, then here's to the men, where'er they be —
   The men of steel and steam!
They're the same old stock from the parent block —
   When they welcomed the wind abeam.
Tho' one shot may equal a broadside's weight,
   One blow may deside the fight,
They serve their guns, they point them straight,
   And the Flag will be kept in sight!
The old captains bold — cocked hats and gold —
   Were made for their country's hour,
And the Soul of the Ship proclaims the mould
   Of the mind in the conning-tower!

Let us sing the song of Wind and Sail—
   Brave deeds of the captains bold!
Never a name but was known to fame,
   And was praised in the days of old.
Let us sing the song of the armored ship,
   With the plunging, roaring bow!
For the Flag is the same, the men are the same —
   'T is the song of Then and Now!

PACK UP YOUR TROUBLES IN YOUR OLD KIT BAG AND SMILE, SMILE, SMILE

GUS ASAF   Music by F. POWELL

Private Perks is a funny little sodger,
With a smile, a funny smile.
Five feet none, he 's an artful little dodger
With a smile, a funny smile.
Flush or broke, he 'll have his little joke,
He can't be suppress'd.
All the other fellows have to grin
When he gets this off his chest, — Hi

CHORUS

Pack up your troubles in your old kit bag
And smile, smile, smile.
While you 've a lucifer to light your fag,
Smile, boys, that 's the style.

What 's the use of worrying,
It 's never worth while, so
Pack up your troubles in your old kit bag,
And smile, smile, smile.

Private Perks went a marching into Flanders,
With his smile, funny smile.
He was loved by the privates and commanders
For his smile, his funny smile.
When a throng of Bosches came along
With a mighty swing,
Perks yell'd out "This little bunch is mine"
Keep your heads down, boys, and sing, Hi

CHORUS

Private Perks he came back from Bosche shooting
With his smile, his funny smile.
Round his home he then set up recruiting,
With his smile, his funny smile.
He told all his pals, the short, the tall,
What a time he 'd had,
And as each enlisted like a man
Private Perks said "Now, my lad," Hi.

CHORUS

PEACE WITH A SWORD[1]

Ense petit placidam sub libertate quietem.   (Motto of Mass.)

First sung to music by Mabel W. Daniels, at a concert of the Handel and Haydn Society, Chorus, Soloists and Orchestra, in Symphony Hall, Boston, February 17, 1918.   Poem was written April, 1917, just before we went into the war.   The chorus has since been sung all over the land.

> Peace! How we love her and the good she brings
>   On broad, benignant wings!
> And we have clung to her, how close and long,
>   While she has made us strong.
> Now we must guard her lest her power cease,
> And in the harried world be no more peace,
>   Even with a sword!
>   Help us, O Lord!
>
> For us no patient peace, the weary goal
>   Of a war-sickened soul!
> No peace that battens on misfortune's pain,
>   Swollen with selfish gain,
> Bending slack knees before a calf of gold,
> With nerveless fingers impotent to hold
>   The freemen's sword:
>   Not this, O Lord!
>
> No peace, bought for us by the martyr dead
>   Of countries reeking red;
> No peace flung to us from the tyrant's hand,
>   Sop to a servile land.
> Our Peace the State's strong arm holds high and free,
> The "placid Peace she seeks in liberty,"
>   Yea, "With a sword."
>   Help us, O Lord!
>
> O Massachusetts! In your golden prime,
>   Not with the bribe of time
> You won her; subtle words and careful ways
>   In perilous days.

[1] This poem and the following one are from "Heart of New England," by Abbie Farwell Brown, Houghton, Mifflin Co., Boston, who kindly gave permission for use in this book.

No! By your valor, by the patriot blood
Of your brave sons poured in a generous flood.
    Peace, with a sword!
    Help us, O Lord.

Fling out the banners that defied a king;
    The tattered colors bring
That made a nation one from sea to sea
    In godly liberty.
Unsheathe the patriot sword in time of need,
O Massachusetts, shouting in the lead, —
    "Peace, with a sword!
    Help us, O Lord!"

PRAYER FOR AMERICA

ABBIE FARWELL BROWN

O Lord of justice and of right
    Who made the generous Cause prevail,
Who helped our heroes win the fight,
    Now let not their endeavor fail.
Facing new dangers that arise,
Oh, make us wise!

Draw out the best of each to serve
    Unselfishly the common good,
Nor let the wider vision swerve
    From the true goal of brotherhood.
To this, thy mighty-blended race,
Oh, give thy grace!

Give us great leaders we can trust
    To strive for righteousness alone;
Cast small ambition in the dust,
    With greed and malice overthrown.
Lord God, preserver of the State,
Oh, make us great!

OH, HOW I HATE TO GET UP IN THE MORNING

Words and music by IRVING BERLIN

The other day I chanced to meet
   A soldier friend of mine.
He 'd been in camp for several weeks
   And he was looking fine;
His muscles had developed
   And his cheeks were rosy red;
I asked him how he liked the life
   And this was what he said:

"Oh, how I hate to get up in the morning,
Oh, how I 'd love to remain in bed,
For the hardest part of all is to hear the bugler call,
'You 've got to get up, you 've got to get up this morning.'
Some day I 'm going to murder the bugler,
Some day they 're going to find him dead;
I 'll amputate his reveille,
And step upon it heavily,
And spend the rest of my life in bed."

A bugler in the army is the luckiest of men,
He wakes the boys at five and then goes back to bed again
He does n't have to blow again until the afternoon
If ev'rything goes well with me
I 'll be a bugler soon.

Oh, how I hate to get up in the morning,
Oh, how I 'd love to remain in bed,
For the hardest blow of all is to hear the bugler call
"You 've got to get up, you 've got to get up this morning."
Oh, boy, the minute the battle is over,
Oh, boy, the minute the foe is dead,
I 'll put my uniform away
And move to Philadelphi-a
And spend the rest of my life in bed.

JOAN OF ARC

Words by ALFRED BRYAN and WILLIE WESTON   Music by JACK WEEKS

Alfred Bryan was born September 15, 1871, Brantford, Canada, and studied French History when a boy, always admiring Joan of Arc ardently. The song was first sung by Willie Weston, Royal Theatre, New York, May 1917.

While you are sleeping, your France is weeping,
Wake from your dreams, maid of France,
Her heart is bleeding, are you unheeding?
Come with the flame in your glance.
Through gates of Heaven, with your sword in hand,
Come your legions to command.

CHORUS

Joan of Arc, Joan of Arc,
Do your eyes, from the skies
    See the foe?
Don't you see the drooping Fleur de Lis
Can't you hear the tears of Normandy
Joan of Arc, Joan of Arc,
Let your spirit guide us through,
Come and lead your France to victory
Joan of Arc, are they calling you?

Alsace is sighing, Lorraine is crying.
Their mother, France, looks to you.
Her sons at Verdun, bearing the burden,
Pray for your coming anew;
At the gates of Heaven, do they bar your way?
Souls that passed through yesterday.

Copyright by Waterson, Berlin & Snyder and reproduced by permission.

SWEET LITTLE BUTTERCUP

Words by ALFRED BRYAN   Music by NORMAN PALEY

Will you miss me little Buttercup,
Said a rustic lad one day,
I must go away, and I must obey.
Come and kiss me, lift your two lips up.
There now, dearie, don't you cry,
Hear the bugles calling;
It is time to say "Goodbye."

REFRAIN

Sweet little Buttercup,
Dry your eyes of blue.
I 'll come back to you
When the war is through.
Safe in your sylvan dell
Far from the shot and shell
Let your love shine, —
Angels guide you, watch beside you
Sweet little Buttercup, mine.

Stop your crying, little Buttercup
Sang a little bird one night;
Stars are shining bright
On his mantle white.
Don't be sighing, lift your spirit up
Soon he will be on his way.
Hear the breezes sighing,
Don't you hear them softly say.

REFRAIN

J. WILL CALLAHAN

Born on a farm near Columbus, Ind., March 17, 1874, he studied law until rheumatism of the eyes made it necessary to abandon his chosen work.

He then took to composing poetry and while living in a little bungalow in the Bay View woods near Petrosky, Mich., dictated to his wife the happy, inspiring words of "Smiles," and remarked when questioned about what a great help his wife had been — "I could n't have made the grade if it had n't been for her. It 's been a long grind to success, but there have been smiles through it all, and the happiest to me have been the 'smiles that drove away the tear drops' from my dear wife's face, when the world reached out and took us in. I love pine-scented northern Michigan. Its solitudes have been my inspiration."

Two of Callahan's songs have been officially adopted by the National Y. M. C. A. and sent to every camp in the United

States, and to all American Expeditionary Force camps abroad. Over two million copies of "Smiles" have been sold, and enormous numbers of records for phonographs.

SMILES

Words by J. WILL CALLAHAN   Music by LEE S. ROBERTS

Dearie, now I know
Just what makes me love you so,
Just what holds me and enfolds me
In its golden glow;
Dearie, now I see
'T is each smile so bright and free,
For life's sadness turns to gladness
When you smile on me.

REFRAIN

There are smiles that make us happy,
    There are smiles that make us blue,
There are smiles that steal away the teardrops
    As the sunbeams steal away the dew.
There are smiles that have a tender meaning,
    That the eyes of love alone may see,
And the smiles that fill my life with sunshine
    Are the smiles that you give to me.

Dearie, when you smile
Everything in life 's worth while.
Love grows fonder as we wander
Down each magic mile;

Cheery melodies
Seem to float upon the breeze,
Doves are cooing while they 're wooing
In the leafy trees.

OVER THERE

GEORGE M. COHAN

Johnnie get your gun, get your gun, get your gun,
Take it on the run, on the run, on the run,
Hear them calling you and me,
Ev'ry son of liberty.
Hurry right away, no delay, go today,
Make your daddy glad to have had such a lad,
Tell your sweetheart not to pine,
To be proud her boy 's in line.

CHORUS

Over there, over there,
Send the word over there
That the Yanks are coming,
The drums rum tumming ev'rywhere,
So prepare, say a prayer,
Send the word to beware,
We 'll be over, we 're coming over
And we won't come back till it 's over,
Over there, over there.

Johnnie get your gun, get your gun, get your gun,
Johnnie, show the Hun you 're a son of a gun,
Hoist the flag and let her fly,
Yankee Doodle do or die.
Pack your kit, show your grit, do your bit,
Yankees to the ranks from the towns and the tanks,
Make your mother proud of you
And the Red, White and Blue.

AMERICAN ARMY HYMN

This beautiful "Hymn" was written by the Rev. Allen Eastman Cross, son of the late Judge David Cross of Manchester,
N. H., and published in the August 9, 1917, issue of *Congregation-
alist and Christian World.* Mr. Cross is the pastor of the Congre-
gational Church at Milford, Mass. His mother, Anna Quacken-

bush Eastman Cross, is one of the charter members of the New Hampshire Society of Colonial Dames of America. At one time he served as assistant to the Rev. George A. Gordon of Boston. Reproduced by special permission of the author.

Air: *Materna*

America, America,
We lift our battle cry!
To live for Thee is more than life,
And more than death to die!
Now by the blood our fathers gave,
And by our God above,
And by the Flag on every grave,
We pledge to Thee our love.

America, America,
Bid all thy banners shine!
O Mother of the mighty dead,
Our very lives are thine.
At Freedom's altar now we stand
For God and Liberty!
Lord, God of Hosts, at Thy command,
We lift our souls to Thee.

America, America,
Speed on, by sea and air!
We take the stripes of sacrifice
The stars of honor dare;
And by the road our fathers trod
We march to victory,
To fight for Freedom and for God,
Till all the world be free.

MOTHERLAND

Tune *Maryland! My Maryland!*
By Rev. Allan Eastman Cross

Oh beautiful! beyond compare,
Motherland! my Motherland!
God make our love for Thee a prayer,
Motherland! my Motherland!

Crusaders for a new Crusade,
Of shame alone we stand afraid—
And shall Thy Glory be betrayed,
    Motherland! my Motherland!

A Vandal host has challenged Thee,
    Motherland! my Motherland!
They hate thy hallowed liberty,
    Motherland! my Motherland!
Now loose the Eagle of thy Might,
And fling the vulture brood to flight,
And free the world for Truth and Right,
    Motherland! my Motherland!

The starry Flag that flies for Thee,
    Motherland! my Motherland!
Salutes the soul that dies for Thee,
    Motherland! my Motherland!
Its flaming folds shall o'er him wave,
Its holy stars shall guard his grave—
The "Glory" he has died to save,
    Motherland! my Motherland!

CRUSADERS — A WAR SONG

By Mrs. Henry W. Eliot (Charlotte C. Eliot), A Colonial Dame of St. Louis, Missouri.
Permission to reprint in this volume was graciously given by the author.
This song was published in the Boston *Herald* in 1917.

Air: *Scots wha hae wi' Wallace Bled*

Sons of free men, once again
Waken to a martial strain,
Haste your birthright to maintain,
Strike for liberty.
Be ye true to those who came,
Lit our country's altar flame,
Through the Ages to proclaim
A land forever free.

Hark, what cry is hither borne
From the lands that war has torn?

'T is the voice of those who mourn,
Who all for freedom gave.
Theirs the sacrifice supreme,
Theirs the vision and the dream,
Yours to finish and redeem,
Yours at last to save.

Once crusaders fought to gain
Christ's sepulchre — ye fight again
Love and mercy to maintain
Christ living to restore.
Where invading hordes oppress
Drive forth the foes of righteousness,
Suffering and wrong redress,
Bring happiness once more.

Lo, from every clime and land,
Heart to heart and hand to hand,
Men are coming to withstand
The tyranny of might.
'T is the Army of the Lord,
Be His righteous wrath outpoured.
Armed with His resistless sword,
His host will conquering fight.

HAIL, HAIL, THE GANG'S ALL HERE

D. A. Esrom

The music of this song is from "The Pirates of Penzance," one of the Gilbert and Sullivan operas, arranged by Louis Russell.

A gang of good fellows are we, are we,
With never a worry you see, you see.
We laugh and we joke, we sing and we smoke,
And live life merrily.
No matter the weather, when we get together
We have a jubilee.

REFRAIN

Hail! Hail! the gang's all here,
What to hell do we care, what to hell do we care,
Hail! Hail! we're full of cheer,
What do we care, Bill! Bill!

We love one another, we do, we do,
With brotherly love, and it's true,
It's one for all, the big and small,
It's always me for you.
No matter the weather, when we get together
We drink a toast or two.

When out for a good time we go,
There's nothing we do that is slow,
Of joy we get our share, you bet,
The gang will tell you so;
No matter the weather, when we get together
We sing this song, — you know.

IT'S A LONG WAY TO BERLIN

Words by ARTHUR FIELDS   Music by LEON FLATOW

Fields is the well known phonograph record singer; Flatow,
former vaudeville performer from Chicago. Both were members
of the New York 71st Regiment, and the song was written to aid
recruiting. It was first sung by Fields August 1, 1917, from a
motor truck in New York city, in his appeal for recruits. The
song was originally called, "I'm feeling fit to do my bit and am
on my way to do it."

Reuben Plank, a husky Yank, came into town one day,
And said, "I can't resist, I really must enlist, by heck,
I'll help to get that Kaiser Bill, I hear so much about."
He passed the test, threw out his chest, and started in to shout.

CHORUS

It 's a long way to Berlin, but we 'll get there.
Uncle Sam will show the way,
Over the line, across the Rhine,
Shouting Hip, Hip, Hurray.
We 'll sing Yankee Doodle "Under the Linden"
With some real live Yankee pep!
It 's a long way to Berlin, but we 'll get there,
And I 'm on my way, by Heck. It 's a Heck.

Reuben Plank was in the ranks for just a little while.
Then he soon went ahead, he 's Corporal Plank instead, by heck.
He gets his squad together, and at night when all is still
They sing the chorus Reuben wrote to Mister Kaiser Bill.

K–K–K–KATY

A stuttering song by GEOFFREY O'HARA

Jimmy was a soldier brave and bold,
Katy was a maid with hair of gold.
Like one act of faith,
Kate was standing at the gate
Watching all the boys on dress parade.
Jimmy with the girls was just a gawk
Stuttered every time he tried to talk;
Still, that night at eight,
He was there, at Katy's gate,
Stuttering to her this lovesick cry.

K-K-K-Katy, beautiful Katy,
You 're the only g-g-g-girl that I adore;
When the m-m-m-moon shines over the cowshed
I 'll be waiting at the k-k-k-kitchen door.

No one ever looked so nice and neat,
No one could be just so cute and sweet.
That 's what Jimmy thought
When the wedding ring he bought.

Now he 's off to France the foe to meet.
Jimmy thought he 'd like to take a chance,
See if he could make the Kaiser dance,
Stepping to a tune, all about the silvery moon —
This is what they hear in far off France.

WHEN THE BOYS COME HOME

Words by JOHN HAY   Music by OLEY SPEAKS

John Hay was one of the most brilliant of American statesmen.
The following poem was written during the time of Mr. Hay's
incumbency as Mr. Lincoln's private secretary.

Mr. Oley Speaks chose this poem because he thought it one
of the finest of all war poems, inasmuch as it dealt with the cheery
side of war. The song was first sung in public by Private Harrold
at the New York Hippodrome. John Philip Sousa conducted his
band in the accompaniment on this occasion. It has been sung
by many of the greatest artists on the concert stage.

There 's a happy time coming when the boys come home,
There 's a glorious day coming when the boys come home;
We will end the dreadful story of the battle dark and gory
In a sunburst of glory, when the boys come home.
The day will seem brighter when the boys come home,
And our hearts will be lighter when the boys come home;
Wives and sweethearts will press them in their arms and caress them,
And pray God to bless them when the boys come home.

The thin ranks will be proudest when the boys come home,
And our cheer will ring the loudest when the boys come home;
The full ranks will be shattered, and the bright arms will be battered,
And the battle standards tattered, when the boys come home.
Their bayonets may be rusty when the boys come home,
And their uniforms be dusty when the boys come home,
But all shall see the traces of battle's royal graces
In the brown and bearded faces when the boys come home.

Our love shall go to meet them when the boys come home,
To bless them and to greet them when the boys come home,
And the fame of their endeavor time and change shall not dissever
From the nation's heart forever, from the nation's heart forever,
From the nation's heart forever, when the boys come home.

THE FLAG

GERTRUDE E. HEATH, M. D.　　　　　　　Music by KATE VANNAH

The Flag Song was written for a Flag-raising at the Plummer
Street School, Gardiner, Maine, in 1899.

Fling out the flag, O children,
　That all the world may see,
How cradled deep in the heart of a child
　The love of the flag may be;
The love of the flag with its crimson bars,
And its field of blue with the spangled stars.

Salute the flag, O children,
　With grave and reverent hand,
For it means far more than the eye can see,
　Your home and your native land;
And men have died for its crimson bars,
And its field of blue with the spangled stars.

Revere the flag, my children,
　Wherever its folds you see,
For cradled deep in the heart of a child,
　The love of the flag may be;
The love of the flag with its crimson bars,
And its field of blue with the spangled stars.

Pray for the flag, my children,
　That never a traitor bold
Defame a bar or a spangled star,
　Or sully a silken fold;
Then pray for the flag with its crimson bars,
And its field of blue with the spangled stars!

Permission to use these verses was kindly given by Dr. Gertrude E. Heath. of Gardiner, Maine.

WHERE DO WE GO FROM HERE, BOYS?

Words by HOWARD JOHNSON   Music by PERCY WENRICH

Paddy Mack drove a hack
  Up and down Broadway;
Pat had one expression and
  He 'd use it ev'ry day;
Any time he 'd grab a fare
  To take them for a ride,
Paddy jumped upon the seat,
  Cracked his whip and cried:

CHORUS

"Where do we go from here, boys,
Where do we go from here?
Anywhere from Harlem to a Jersey City pier."
When Pat would spy a pretty girl,
He 'd whisper in her ear,
"Oh joy, Oh boy, where do we go from here?"

One fine day on Broadway,
  Pat was driving fast
When the street was blown to pieces
  By a subway blast;
Down the hole poor Paddy went,
  A-thinking of his past;
Then he says, says he,
  I think these words will be my last:

CHORUS

"Where do we go from here, boys,
Where do we go from here?"
Paddy's neck was in the wreck,
But still he had no fear;
He saw a dead man next to him
And whispered in his ear,
"Oh joy, Oh boy, where do we go from here?"

First of all at the call,
When the war began,
Pat enlisted in the army
As a fighting man ;
When the drills began,
They 'd walk a hundred miles a day
Tho' the rest got tired,
Paddy always used to say :

CHORUS

"Where do we go from here, boys,
Where do we go from here ?
Slip a pill to Kaiser Bill
And make him shed a tear ;
And when we see the enemy
We 'll shoot him in the rear
Oh joy, Oh boy, where do we go from here ?"

Copyright by Leo Feist, Inc., and reproduced by special permission.

Two songs of British origin were so universally sung by soldiers of the allied armies, and by civilians during the Great War, that every book of war songs should contain them — "Tipperary" and "Keep the Home Fires Burning." "Tipperary" has no touch of war in it, but has a swinging melody, and was an excellent marching song.

There are several accounts of its origin, but the most authentic seems to show that the song was written by Jack Judge, a singer of the English music halls. It was, after several rejections, published by Bert Feldman in London in 1912. At first the sales were disappointing, but when the war broke out and the British troops went to Belgium singing this song upon the march, it spread all over the English-speaking world.

IT 'S A LONG, LONG WAY TO TIPPERARY
Written and composed by JACK JUDGE and HARRY WILLIAMS

Up to mighty London came an Irishman one day,
As the streets are paved with gold, sure everyone was gay,
Singing songs of Piccadilly, Strand and Leicester Square,
Till Paddy got excited, then he shouted to them there:

CHORUS

It 's a long way to Tipperary,
It 's a long way to go;
It 's a long way to Tipperary,
To the sweetest girl I know;
Goodbye, Piccadilly,
Farewell, Leicester Square,
It 's a long, long way to Tipperary,
But my heart 's right there!

Paddy wrote a letter to his Irish Molly O'
Saying, "Should you not receive it, write and let me know!"
"If I make mistakes in 'spelling,' Molly dear," said he,
"Remember it 's the pen that 's bad, don't lay the blame on me."

CHORUS

Molly wrote a neat reply to Irish Paddy O'
Saying, "Mike Maloney wants to marry me, and so
Leave the Strand and Piccadilly, or you 'll be to blame,
For love has fairly drove me silly, hoping you 're the same!"

CHORUS

Next in popularity to "Tipperary" came "Keep the Home Fires Burning," which is said to have been written in ten minutes, by Ivor Novello and Mrs. Guillbertford, to take the place of "Tipperary," which had become tiresome. Mrs. Lena Guillbertford, who built up the words around Novello's music and idea, was an American who formerly lived in Elmira, N. Y., but was killed in 1918 in one of the German air raids on London.

KEEP THE HOME FIRES BURNING

Words by Mrs. Lena Guillbertford   Music by Ivor Novello

They were summoned from the hillside,
They were called in from the glen,
And the country found them ready
At the stirring call for men.
Let no tears add to the hardship
As the soldiers pass along,
And although your heart is breaking
Make it sing this cheery song.

CHORUS

Keep the home fires burning,
While your hearts are yearning,
Though your lads are far away,
They dream of home.
There's a silver lining,
Through the dark cloud shining,
Turn the dark cloud inside out,
Till the boys come home.

Over seas there came a pleading,
"Help a nation in distress"
And we gave our glorious laddies
Honor bade us do no less.
For no gallant son of freedom
To a tyrant's yoke should bend,
And a noble heart must answer
To the sacred call of "Friend."

FOR YOUR BOY AND MY BOY

Words by Gus Kahn   Music by Egbert Van Alstyne

Hear the bugle call
The call for arms for Liberty,
See them one and all
They go to fight for you and me.

Heroes we will find them
  Ev'ry mother's son.
We must get behind them
  Till their work is done.

CHORUS

For your boy and my boy
  And all of the boys out there,
Let's lend our money to the U. S. A.
  And do our share.
Ev'ry bond we're buying
  Will help to hold the fighting line,
Buy bonds, buy bonds,
  For your boy and mine.

Hear the bugle call,
  The call to those who stay at home.
You are soldiers all,
  Though you may never cross the foam.
Keep Old Glory waving
  Proudly up above,
Praying, working, saving
  For the ones you love.

CHORUS

For your boy and my boy
  And all the boys out there,
Let's get together till they come back home
  And do our share.
Ev'ry bond that we are buying
  Will help the boys to cross the Rhine
Buy bonds, buy bonds
  For your boy and mine.

WHAT ARE YOU GOING TO DO TO HELP THE BOYS?

Words by GUS KAHN   Music by EGBERT VAN ALSTYNE

Your Uncle Sam is calling now on ev'ry one of you,
If you're too old or young to fight there's something else to do;
If you have done a bit before don't let the matter rest,
For Uncle Sam expects that ev'ry man will do his best.

What are you going to do for Uncle Sammy?
What are you going to do to help the boys?
If you mean to stay at home while they 're fighting o'er the foam
The least that you can do is buy a Liberty Bond or two!
If you 're going to be a sympathetic miser,
The kind that only lends a lot of noise,
You 're no better than the one who loves the Kaiser —
So what are you going to do to help the boys?

It makes no diff'rence who you are or whence you came, or how,
Your Uncle Sammy help'd you then, and you must help him now.
Your brothers will be fighting for your freedom over there,
And if you love the Stars and Stripes then you must do your share.

Copyright by Jerome H. Remick & Co., and reproduced by special permission.

THERE 'S A LONG, LONG TRAIL

Words by STODDARD KING   Music by ZO ELLIOTT

Nights are growing very lonely,
   Days are very long;
I 'm a growing weary only
   List'ning for your song.
Old remembrances are thronging
   Through my memory,
Till it seems the world is full of dreams
   Just to call you back to me.

There 's a long, long trail a winding
   Into the land of my dreams,
Where the nightingales are singing,
   And a white moon beams.
There 's a long, long night of waiting
   Until my dreams all come true;
Till the day when I 'll be going down
   That long, long trail with you.

Copyright by M. Witmark & Sons, and reproduced by special permission.

All night long I hear you calling,
  Calling sweet and low;
Seem to hear your footsteps falling,
  Everywhere I go.
Tho' the road between us stretches
  Many a weary mile,
I forget that you 're not with me yet
  When I think I see you smile.

CHORUS

THE RED, WHITE AND BLACK

Words by RUTH LAWRENCE, a Member of the New York Society
Permission to reprint in this volume was given by the author.
Air: *Columbia, the Gem of the Ocean*

The Kaiser was counting his conquests,
  When on high he espied Union Jack,
And he called out to Bethmann von Hollweg,
  "Shall we stand mit the Red, White and Black,
Oh! Gerard has gone safe o'er the ocean
  And Roosevelt is coming, I fear;
The Vaterland knows my devotion
  But, Hollweg, I feel mighty queer."

CHORUS

Shall we stand mit the Red, White and Black,
You may stand mit the Red, White and Black;
But call me a special for Berlin,
For, Hollweg, I want to get back.

The Kaiser was sure he was dreaming
  As he gazed once again at the sky
Where the colors of France he saw streaming,
  As the aeroplanes floated by.
Astride on his eagle appearing,
  Uncle Sam was a glorious sight,
Through the thick of the fight, lightly steering
  While von Hindenberg's army took flight.

CHORUS

Away with the Red, White and Black!
  Willy Nilly will never get back
Do you get me, remarked our brave uncle,
  Then believe me, you 'll never get back.

Now safe in the Tower of London
  Is Willy the War-Lord on view,
And 'Arry is paying a shilling
  To see him, and 'Arriet too.
And in Berlin the tricolor 's flying
  And the Eagle is screaming with glee,
And the people in rapture are crying
  "At last we are free, we are free."

CHORUS

Farewell to the Red, White and Black,
Farewell to the Red, White and Black;
Uncle Sam and his allies forever,
Farewell to the Red, White and Black.

JUST A BABY'S PRAYER AT TWILIGHT

Words by SAM M. LEWIS and JOE YOUNG   Music by M. K. JEROME

I 've heard the prayers of mothers,
  Some of them old and gray;
I 've heard the prayers of others
  For those who went away.
Ofttimes a prayer will teach one
  The meaning of "Goodbye";
I felt the pain of each one,
  But this one made me cry.

CHORUS

Just a baby's prayer at twilight,
When lights are low;
Poor baby's years are filled with tears;
There 's a mother there at twilight, who 's proud to know
Her precious little tot is Dad's forget-me-not.

After saying "Goodnight, Mamma,"
She climbs upstairs, quite unawares
And says her prayers.
"Oh, kindly tell my Daddy that he must take care."
That 's a baby's prayer at twilight
For her daddy "over there."

The gold that some folks pray for
   Brings nothing but regrets.
Some day this gold won't pay for
   Their many life-long debts.
Some prayers may be neglected
   Beyond the Golden Gates;
But when they 're all collected,
   Here 's one that never waits.

THE OLD GREY MARE[1]

FRANK PANELLA

The Old Grey Mare was written by Frank Panella and was one of the important songs of the World War and today is used as the official marching song of numerous American Legion Posts.

One American Legion Post from Brownwood, Texas, attends all of the American Legion National conventions, with their own "Old Grey Mare Band" of forty pieces, headed by a beautiful girl riding on an old grey mare.

It is regretted that on account of the copyright today we are unable to give the words of this well-known song.

Another popular war song, "Good-bye, Broadway; Hello, France," was written on the impulse of the moment. Francis Reisner said to his writing partner, William Baskette: "Billy, I 've a great title for a patriotic song." "What is it?" he asked. The answer was, "Good-bye, Broadway; Hello, France."

"The construction of the song began that very moment," says Mr. Baskette, "for the title sounded wonderful to me. Perhaps I worked under that inspiration. At any rate, while I have written a number of other songs, patriotic and otherwise in character — some of them very successful — this one seems to have carried me away somehow — and apparently it has affected other people in the same way. That experience, however, is not at all an unusual one in the life of a song-writer. He may write twenty-five songs, all apparently equally good; then comes the twenty-sixth, and behold! for no especial reason that he can see, it is the 'hit' of his life.

"Owing to the fact that the majority of our soldiers and sailors must pass through New York city before taking their leave across the waters, and that millions of boys were saying good-bye to their loved ones, as well as their country, some of them never to return again, was the cause of the inspiration. The song is now next to the biggest hit the country has ever seen."

GOOD-BYE, BROADWAY; HELLO, FRANCE!

Words by C. Francis Reisner and Benny Davis

Music by Billy Baskette

Good-bye, New York town, good-bye, Miss Liberty,
Your light of freedom will guide us across the sea,
Ev'ry soldier's sweetheart bidding good-bye,
Ev'ry soldier's mother drying her eye.
Cheer up, we 'll soon be there,
Singing this Yankee air:

CHORUS

Good-bye, Broadway; Hello, France,
We 're ten million strong,
Good-bye sweethearts, wives and mothers,
It won't take us long,
Don't you weary while we 're there,
It 's for you we 're fighting too,
So Good-bye, Broadway; Hello, France,
We 're going to square our debt to you.

"Vive Pershing" is the cry across the sea,
We're united in this fight for Liberty.
France sent us a soldier, brave Lafayette
Whose deeds and fame we cannot forget;
Now that we have the chance
We'll pay our debt to France.

CHORUS

Good-bye, Broadway, Hello, France,
    We're ten million strong,
Good-bye sweethearts, wives and mothers,
    It won't take us long,
Don't you weary while we're there,
    It's you we're fighting for;
So Good-bye, Broadway; Hello, France
    We're going to help you win this war.

THE AVIATOR'S HYMN
Written June 3, 1918

Words by SALLY NELSON ROBINS, died Feb. 4, 1925. Vice-President of the Virginia Society, Historian of the National Society of the Colonial Dames, Officer of the Virginia Antiquities Societies. Written by Mrs. Robins at Richmond, Virginia, June 3, 1918.

Permission given by Mrs. Robins especially for this volume.

Air: *Eternal Father, Strong to Save*

Adopted by many states as the State Hymn and sung all during the war, here and abroad, at funerals of aviators.

Almighty Sov'reign of the sky,
Whose ever-wake yet tireless eye,
Counts ev'ry star in distant space,
And holds each planet in its place —
Great Father, give thy tender care,
To Thy Crusaders of the air!

Dear Jesu, whom the angel-band
Held safe-uplifted in its hand,
When Satan's challenge mocked Thy power
To sanctify a bitter hour —
Blest Jesu, let Thy angels care
For Thy Crusaders of the air!

Consoling Spirit, Whose bright ray,
Illumined Pentecostal Day
And gave to Parthian and to Mede,
The blessing of a simple creed —
Beyond the clouds, defend and care
For Thy Crusaders of the air!

Triune of love and life and might,
Direct our soldiers in their flight,
Oh, Father, Son and Holy Ghost,
Strengthen that brave, ascending host —
With love, faith, consolation, care!
Thy bold Crusaders of the air.

IN LANDS ACROSS THE SEA

By Rev. Louis F. Benson, 1917

Special permission to print in this volume given by the author

Let freemen's hearts grow bolder;
  Let freedom's banner fly
Where God's four winds unfold her
  To God's uncharted sky.
His Word and not another's
  Is pledged to liberty;
His hand hath made men brothers,
  His truth shall make men free.

Where freedom's flag is flying
  In lands across the sea,
On Thee we are relying,
  Great God, we count on Thee!
For right is right for ever,
  Though men have crowned the wrong,
And truth shall perish never—
  Great God, how long? how long?

When our brave lads are dying
 In lands across the sea,
On Thee we are relying,
 Great God, they die for Thee!
And if we lay them sleeping
 In lands beyond the sea,
God have them in Thy keeping —
 We leave them there with Thee.

HEROES' HYMN

Amy Sherman Bridgman

O Thou, Jehovah, Sovereign in battle,
Stoop to our sorrow, hear us we pray
Grant us Thy solace, give us Thy comfort,
One mighty nation, mourning to-day!

Loudly cried Freedom; to Her they answered, —
Here, in our anguish, yet speaks our pride, —
To Her we gave them; Thou couldst not save them;
For Her they battled; for Her they died.

From Her their crowning; to Her their choral;
Deathless their glory; boundless their sky;
Grant them Thy guerdon; give us Thy comfort
O God of Nations, to Thee we cry!

Mrs. William Henry Root received a letter from her husband, Lieut. William Henry Root of Battery A, 102d Field Artillery, American Expeditionary Forces, in which he stated that the Haverhill boys of Battery A were on a big transport carrying 1500 men, which arrived at its destination without mishap. The letter did not state where the soldiers on this transport landed, but it is presumed to be "somewhere in France." Lieut. Root stated that the transports were heavily convoyed and these naval ships did wonderfully effective work. In proceeding through the war zone all the men wore life belts and the soldiers and sailors were not allowed to speak a word. The ships also were without lights.

Lieutenant Root said that all the men were cheerful and in good health. On the second day out from an American port a man fell overboard, but was quickly rescued, with no ill effects. He did not say who the soldier was or whether he was from Haverhill.

While on shipboard Lieutenant Root sang two stanzas of a composition, "The Soldier's Pledge" to the tune of "O Promise Me." After the entertainment General Parker, who was on board, complimented the officer and shook hands with him. The men indulged in sports and drills while on shipboard and found plenty to keep them busy.

Lieutenant Root said that there was much that could be told but the present was perhaps inopportune and the boys would have something to tell about when they arrived home that would be of the keenest interest to all. He also said that the letter would arrive on the same ship in which the Haverhill men went over.

THE SOLDIER'S PLEDGE

Words by Lieut. William Henry Root   Air: *Oh, Promise Me*

America, thy sacred flag we bear
Across the stormy seas against the foe.
America, with lifted sword we swear
That all the peoples of the world may know:
That freedom shall not perish from the earth;
That justice and humanity shall live;
That joy and peace shall have another birth;
And this we swear, America.

America, the thunder of thy guns,
Thy fleets, ten thousand airmen in the skies
Shall show thy boastful enemy, the Huns,
That victory follows where the eagle flies.
Heroic France and England by our side,
We pledge our lives for victory and fame.
The Great Republic shall not be denied;
And this we swear, America.

WE ARE A RACE OF FREEMEN

Marching Song for the Mississippi Regiments in the American Army.
By ERON DUNBAR ROWLAND, a member of the Mississippi Society of
Colonial Dames.

Special permission to reprint in this volume was given by the author.

This poem has been pronounced by a number of able critics
one of the best so far written about the American Army. It
was composed for a marching song for the Mississippi troops when
volunteers were called for at the beginning of our war with Ger-
many for freedom and humanity.

We are a race of freemen, united heart and hand,
  For liberty and justice unyieldingly we stand;
And as our patriot fathers died for the truth of yore
  Our hosts are marching forward in freedom's cause once more.

CHORUS

Huzza for America! Huzza! Huzza!
  Beneath her starry banner we rally from afar,
From mountain, plain and valley we come, we come, huzza!
  For God and right and freedom we wage a righteous war —
Woe to the haughty tyrant who would our pathway bar.

To break the chains of tyranny, to heal oppression's woe
  With grim, avenging faces our mighty legions go,
Till every curse is lifted by cruel despot breathed
  And every wrong is righted our sword shall be unsheathed.

CHORUS

Huzza for America! Huzza! Huzza!
  Beneath her starry banner we rally from afar,
From mountain, plain and valley we come, we come, huzza!
  For God and right and freedom we wage a righteous war —
Woe to the haughty tyrant who would our pathway bar.

THE UNFURLING OF THE FLAG

Words by Clara Endicott Sears · · · Music by John Hopkins Densmore

This poem was written by Miss Clara Endicott Sears at the same time in which Congress had its all night session to decide on whether America should enter the war, that is, the night of April 5–6, 1917. The music for it was composed by John Hopkins Densmore, and it was first sung in public on Memorial Day, 1917, by fifteen hundred school children at the Memorial services of Edward W. Kingsley, Post 113, Mass. G. A. R., at Ford Hall, Boston.

There 's a streak across the sky line
  That is gleaming in the sun,
Watchers from the light-house towers
Signalled it to foreign Powers
  Just as daylight had begun,
    Message thrilling,
    Hopes fulfilling
  To those fighting o'er the seas.
"It 's the flag we 've named Old Glory
  That 's unfurling to the breeze."

Can you see the flashing emblem
  Of our Country's high ideal?
Keep your lifted eyes upon it
And draw joy and courage from it,
  For it stands for what is real,
    Freedom's calling
    To the falling
  From oppression's hard decrees.
It 's the flag we 've named Old Glory
  You see floating in the breeze.

Glorious flag we raise so proudly,
  Stars and stripes, red, white and blue.
You have been the inspiration
Of an ever-growing nation
  Such as this world never knew.

Peace and Justice,
Freedom, Progress,
Are the blessings we can seize
When the flag we call Old Glory
Is unfurling to the breeze.

When the cry of battling nations
Reaches us across the space
Of the wild tumultuous ocean,
Hearts are stirred with deep emotion
For the saving of the race !
Peace foregoing,
Aid bestowing,
Bugles blowing,
First we drop on bended knees,
Then with shouts our grand Old Glory
We set flaunting to the breeze !

Permission courteously granted by the author.

AMERICA, HERE 'S MY BOY

Words by ANDREW B. STERLING   Music by ARTHUR LANGE

There 's a million mothers knocking at the nation's door,
A million mothers, yes, and there 'll be more;
And while within each mother heart they pray,
Just hark what one brave mother has to say : —

CHORUS

America, I raised a boy for you
America, You 'll find him staunch and true,
Place a gun upon his shoulder,
He is ready to die or do.
America, he is my only one, my hope, my pride and joy,
But if I had another, he would march beside his brother.

MADELON

Lyric by Louis Bousquet   Music by Camille Robert
English Version by Alfred Bryan

There is a tavern way down in Brittany
Where weary soldiers take their liberty
The keeper's daughter, whose name is Madelon,
Pours out the wine while they laugh and "carry on,"
And while the wine goes to their senses,
 Her sparkling glance goes to their hearts,
Their admiration so intense is
 Each one his tale of love imparts.
She coquettes with them all but favors none at all
And here 's the way they banter ev'ry time they call.

CHORUS

O Madelon, you are my only one
O Madelon, now that the foe is gone
Let the wedding bells ring sweet and gay
Let this be our wedding day,
O Madelon, sweet maid of Normandy,
Like Joan of Arc you'll always be to me
All thru life for you I'll carry on,
Madelon, Madelon, Madelon.

He was a fair hair'd boy from Brittany
She was a blue eyed maid from Normandy,
He said good-bye, to this pretty Madelon,
He went his way with the boys who carry on;
And when his noble work was ended
 He said farewell to his command
Back to his Madelon he wended
 To claim her little heart and hand.
With love-light in his glance, this gallant son of France
He murmurs as she listens with her heart entranc'd —

CHORUS

LAND OF OUR HEARTS

Words by JOHN HALL INGHAM, Philadelphia.
Permission to print in this volume given by the author.
Music composed by the late GEORGE WILLIAM WARREN, of New York, for
the hymn "Rise, Crowned with Light."

Originally written for a literary club, of which the author was
a member.

During the World War it was sung in the Chapel at West Point
and became popular in the military training camps in the United
States.

Prof. George W. Chadwick developed the song for a cantata
which was performed by a large chorus and the New York Phil-
harmonic Orchestra.

> Land of the North, where battling breezes sweep
> O'er Arctic snow and pine-encircled steep,
> And thunderous torrents wrestle in the air, —
> Yield us the strength to suffer and to dare!
>
> Land of the South, where odorous warmth pervades
> Forests of palm and ever verdant glades,
> Gold-fruited groves, wide acres crowned with white, —
> Shed on our lives thy sweetness and thy light!
>
> Land of the East, where erst our fathers trod,
> Vowing the soil to Freedom and to God,
> More we demand than wealth of mine and mart, —
> Grant us high aims, true Wisdom, noble Art!
>
> Land of the West the pioneer hath won,
> Following the promise, guided by the sun, —
> From gleaming grain, from sky-ascending slope,
> Point to the future, sanctify our hope!
>
> Land of our Hearts, upon whose bounteous breast
> Earth's weary sons from many lands find rest,
> Bind us in love, that we may truly be
> One blood, one Nation, everlastingly!

This volume may well be concluded with the song above, which
Mr. Ingham regards as an "End-of-War Song." The feeling that
hope for the future and love and trust must be the guiding forces
which will make possible the response to Mr. Ingham's exhortation for "one blood, one nation, everlastingly," will undoubtedly
be shared by all who read this book.

ALPHABETICAL LIST OF THE WAR SONGS

INDEX

INDEX